LIFE SCIENCE LIBRARY

MATTER

OTHER BOOKS
BY THE
EDITORS OF LIFE

LIFE SCIENCE LIBRARY

CONSULTING EDITORS

René Dubos
Henry Margenau
C. P. Snow

MATTER

by Ralph E. Lapp
and the Editors of LIFE

TIME INCORPORATED, NEW YORK

THE AUTHOR

RALPH E. LAPP has played an unusual dual role in the atomic age. A physicist who participated in the development of the atom bomb, he has been a pioneer interpreter of science as a consultant to government, industry and, in his lectures, articles and books, to the layman. He has published nine books ranging from the widely used textbook *Nuclear Radiation Physics* to such bestsellers as *Kill and Overkill*, an analysis of the critical problems faced in shaping defense policy in an H-bomb era.

THE CONSULTING EDITORS

RENE DUBOS, member and professor of The Rockefeller Institute, is a microbiologist and experimental pathologist world-famous for his pioneering in antibiotics, including the discovery of tyrothricin. He has written, among other books, *Mirage of Health* and *The Dreams of Reason*.

HENRY MARGENAU is Eugene Higgins professor of physics and natural philosophy at Yale and an editor of the *American Journal of Science*. His books include *Open Vistas* and *The Nature of Physical Reality*. He has made noteworthy contributions in spectroscopy and nuclear physics.

C. P. SNOW has won an international audience for his novels, including *The New Men*, *The Search* and *The Affair*, which explore the scientist's role in our society. Trained as a physicist, he was chief of scientific personnel for Britain's Ministry of Labour in World War II. He was knighted in 1957.

ON THE COVER

Golden crystals form from sulphur, the "brimstone" of the Bible. Most of the other 88 natural elements known today were discovered in relatively recent centuries. On the back cover are five early chemical symbols for elements devised by the 19th Century Englishman John Dalton. Clockwise, they represent hydrogen, alumine, potash, oxygen, sulphur.

CONTENTS

TIME INC. BOOK DIVISION

Editor:
Norman P. Ross

Copy Director: *Art Director:*
William Jay Gold   Edward A. Hamilton

Chief of Research:
Beatrice T. Dobie

EDITORIAL STAFF FOR "MATTER"

Editor, LIFE Science Library: George McCue
Text Editor: Diana Hirsh
Assistants to the Editor: Tom Alexander, John MacDonald,
Robert G. Mason, William Olcott
Designer: Arnold C. Holeywell
Staff Writers: Stephen Espie, Alfred Lansing, Harvey B. Loomis, Paul Trachtman
Chief Researcher: Sheila Osmundsen
Researchers: David Beckwith, Valentin Y. L. Chu, Joan C. Coates, Doris C. Coffin,
Mollie Cooper, Eleanor W. Engelmann, Elizabeth Evans, Emily Heine,
John L. Hochmann, Leonard Lipton, Beatrice S. Mathews, Robert R. McLaughlin,
Renée S. Pickèl, Victor H. Waldrop
Picture Researchers: Margaret K. Goldsmith, Joan Lynch
Art Associate: Robert L. Young
Art Assistants: James D. Smith, W. Lee Einhorn,
Charles Mikolaycak, Douglas B. Graham
Copy Staff: Marian Gordon Goldman, Suzanne Seixas, Dolores A. Littles

Publisher: Jerome S. Hardy
General Manager: John A. Watters

LIFE MAGAZINE

Editor: Edward K. Thompson
Managing Editor: George P. Hunt
Publisher: C. D. Jackson

The text for the chapters of this book was written by Ralph E. Lapp, for the picture essays by the editorial staff. Valuable assistance in the production of the book was contributed by: Doris O'Neil, Chief of the LIFE Picture Library; Clara Applegate of the TIME-LIFE News Service; Margaret Sargent, LIFE film editor; and Content Peckham, Chief of the Time Inc. Bureau of Editorial Reference.

INTRODUCTION

NOT TOO long ago one took it on faith that the final scientific picture of the world would be beautiful, orderly and simple. As it has continued to be sketched in, we have had a number of surprises. The beauty is there, but not of the expected kind. The order is there, but not of the sort to damp down our questions. The simplicity has disappeared.

No better case in point can be offered than the subject of this book. Matter *is* the world around us; it is everything we see and feel and touch. It seems thoroughly familiar—until we read in the following pages what the scientists have discovered about it within the last 50 years, the last 20, the last 2. The diamond, for example, seems on the face of it resplendently substantial. But as we read on, we find that the diamond is a patterned arrangement of atoms which are themselves mainly empty space, with infinitesimal dabs of electrons whirling round infinitesimal dabs of protons and neutrons. All this we now know to be matter, but we are by no means sure the picture is complete. Within the minuscule heart of the atom—the nucleus—have been found no fewer than 30 kinds of elementary particle, and no one can say what more will emerge under nuclear bombardment. The further scientists analyze, the less obvious the answers become.

The mysteries of matter have stimulated the great intellectual exploration of our time. There are two reasons why we should share in its excitements. One is for the sheer fun, the esthetic pleasure, call it what you like, of reaching deeper into the unknown. The other is for the understanding to be gained as a result.

This understanding we ought to possess not only per se but also for the power it puts in our hands. Perceiving the nature of matter, we can control it for our own purposes, lethal or benevolent. A lump of uranium ore looks as quiescent as any other old lump of rock. The first inquiries into the structure of these lumps seemed just another academic exercise. Yet, within a generation, governments were spending billions of dollars on scientific projects, not so academic, which were a direct outcome of the first innocent experiments. For it happened that scientists had stumbled on a way to release amounts of energy that men had never before had at their command. The results have shaped the course of world history for 20 years.

Something like this may happen again. It is more likely to happen than not. And while scientists and statesmen may finally make the decisions that become necessary, ordinary responsible citizens will first have to make their own thoughts felt. They will be unable to do so unless they comprehend what is going on. Science will give us a better world only if enough people make sure that it does so, which means that we must, to begin with, acquire the knowledge that helps us understand. This book is a step in that direction.

C. P. Snow

1

An Endless
Searching for
Substance

SEVERAL million years ago a primitive precursor of man came upon a hand-sized stone which the accidents of erosion had shaped with a sharp edge. Wielding this strange implement, he found it equally good for whittling a branch or besting an enemy.

In June 1962, physicists at the 33-billion-electron-volt atom-smashing synchrotron at Brookhaven, Long Island, fired atomic particles through 42 feet of armor plate and discovered the existence of two different varieties of the neutrino, a mysterious and elusive particle as close to nothing as anything can get, and so penetrating that it can shoot through 100 trillion miles of lead like a bullet through a cloud.

Although eons apart in time and intelligence, early man with his simple stone and modern man with his complex synchrotron were engaged in the same endeavor: the investigation of matter. They differed only in intent. The first sought merely to use matter; his civilized successor seeks to understand it.

The study of matter has taught man how to cook, clothe himself, make tools, clear wilderness, till land, build cities, journey across oceans and soar into outer space. It has given him, on the one hand, the means of destroying himself in thermonuclear war; on the other hand, the hope of some day lifting his greatest curse, poverty, by harnessing the heavy hydrogen energy of the sea.

Yet, for all we have learned about matter, some of its fundamental mysteries persist. The more scientists probe, the greater complexities they encounter. They now know, for instance, that almost nothing, even the hardest diamond, is really solid; that the atom itself—the heart of matter—is mostly empty space; and that if each atom were collapsed into a sphere no bigger than its own core, or nucleus, then all the bulk of the Washington Monument could be crammed into a space smaller than the eraser on a pencil.

What *is* matter?

"Whatever occupies space," says the dictionary; "that which is considered to constitute the substance of the physical universe. . . ." The earth, the seas, the breeze, the sun, the stars—everything that man surveys, can touch or feel—is matter. So is man himself. Fittingly, the very word derives from the Latin *mater,* mother. Matter is as hard as steel, as yielding as a pool of water, as formless as the invisible oxygen in the air. Each of its three familiar states—solid, liquid and gas—can change into each of the other states at different temperatures. But whatever its form, all matter is made up of the same basic entities—atoms.

The atom itself is so small as to numb the imagination. Its diameter is less than a hundred millionth of an inch; it would take more than a million of them, edge to edge, to match the thickness of this page. Within the atom, like a diamond nested in cotton fluff, is its central nucleus—only

THE POWER IN A ROCK
Man's age-old inquisitiveness about matter has paid off handsomely. The rock being inspected opposite by a student at the National Youth Conference on the Atom in 1961 is a piece of uranium ore. When discovered in 1789 uranium seemed no more than a dull, gray, useless metal, but it has since become the coveted source of atomic energy for war and peace.

about a hundred thousandth of the atom in diameter, yet accounting for 99.9 per cent of its entire "mass"—its full substance. Within the nucleus dwell two of the atom's three kinds of building blocks, the proton and neutron. Outside the nucleus is the third kind, the electron. Like planets around the sun—indeed the distance between the atom's inner and outer ramparts is relatively many times greater than that between sun and earth—electrons endlessly circle the nucleus, at breakneck speed, held captive to it by its attractive electrical force. Comprising less than 0.1 per cent of the atom's mass, electrons are a sort of atomic afterthought, but they are what give the atom its basic personality.

A kinship of pianos and pennies

Every atom has the same basic internal structure, and the protons, neutrons and electrons in any one atom are identical to those in any other atom. This holds true whether the atom resides in a piano or a penny. The atoms of one element differ from those of another element only in the *number* of their protons and electrons; it is this difference in number that makes an element—whether liquid, solid or gas—what it is.

Despite all that man has unmasked of matter, his efforts go on apace. The U.S. government alone is now spending almost $500 million a year on basic research in the purely physical sciences. In essence this is a voyage of discovery—mainly through the channels of physics and chemistry—into matter's still-uncharted realms. So complicated has the undertaking become that its participants are no longer known simply as physicists or chemists, but as analytical chemists, radiochemists, nuclear physicists, solid-state physicists, astrophysicists, crystallographers and plasmologists—to name but a few of the proliferating specialties.

Even now their efforts have transformed our lives beyond recall. Our food preservatives, our synthetic fabrics, our rockets, jets and nuclear weapons were born of inquiries by chemists and physicists into the behavior and structure of matter. Computer systems and transistor radios were born of inquiries by solid-state specialists into the type of solids known as semiconductors; the current concern of these men with "microelectronics" may soon make possible a whole electronic circuit on the head of a pin, and has already produced a phonograph amplifier about one twentieth the size of a dime.

Prodigious as are these victories over matter, the possibility of further conquest irresistibly beckons. Scientists are exploring the so-called "fourth state of matter," plasma, which emerges when the third state, gas, is heated to temperatures of several thousand degrees. In the plasma state, particles rove unrestrained and irascibly individualistic. Could plasma particles of such light substances as hydrogen be compelled to unite, their vast potential energy would be released; if confined and

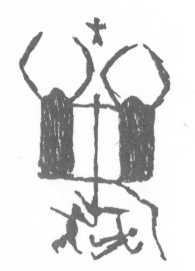

AN EARTHY USE FOR BRONZE
This drawing of two long-horned oxen pulling a plow, with three farmers in attendance, was scratched on a rock in the Italian Alps some time in the Bronze Age. It was during this period of prehistory that man first hammered and cast bronze into such implements as plowshares. The alloy, the first made by man, is composed of a mixture of copper and tin: the more tin, the stronger the bronze.

A DIVINE COPPER MINE
Gods and goddesses engage in manual labor in the copper mine shown on this Greek clay tablet of the Sixth Century B.C. Hermes wields an ax *(right)*. Amphitrite loads ore *(center)* and Poseidon hands a basket of it to a slim young goddess *(left)*. Among the first metals bent to man's will, copper was discovered in the form of pure metal nuggets during the New Stone Age, about 8000 B.C.

thereby controlled, this energy would supply the world's needs for some 20 billion years.

Controlled fusion of plasma particles cannot be achieved at a practicable rate except at the incredible temperature of 180,000,000°F. (by comparison, the sun's core at 25,000,000°F., is a mite chilly). Confinement of the superheated plasma cannot be achieved within any material container. Yet despite these formidable obstacles, progress is astir. For fractions of a second, both U.S. and Russian scientists have managed to heat plasma to some 70,000,000°F. Moreover, researchers believe that they may be able to confine the plasma within a magnetic field suitably shaped as a "nonmaterial" bottle; in the U.S. and Russian experiments, some plasma was actually contained for a very brief instant.

Along another frontier of matter, probers are pondering the crystal— the orderly, latticelike body into which the atoms of many solids arrange themselves. Most crystalline latticeworks contain imperfections; a crystal without flaw would be the strongest substance known. Some metallurgists and solid-state physicists, indeed, feel that constructing a single, large, absolutely pure metallic crystal would rank with splitting the atom as a scientific accomplishment. And they may be edging toward that end. Certain short circuits in radio and telephone systems have been traced to odd growths of ultrafine crystalline hairs on the metallic surfaces involved, in one case cadmium, in another, zinc plating. Similar "whiskers" have since been found on many other metals, and also laboratory-grown under varying atmospheric conditions. Why these peculiar little growths form is still unknown, but their potential is under careful scrutiny, and for good reason. A whisker of iron, for example, has a tensile strength of nearly two million pounds per square inch; bridges and skyscrapers fantastically stronger than today's, yet requiring much less material, could be erected if iron of such quality were made abundant.

The ultimate quarry

But however absorbing these aspects of the pursuit of matter, the scientists' main quarry remains unchanged. They are, in short, still on the hunt for the basic answer to what *is* matter—what makes the elementary electron, proton and neutron particles of the atom assume their form and behave as they do. In their forays deeper and deeper into the atom, they are using machines undreamed of decades ago: vastly powerful, immensely expensive atom-smashers, or "particle accelerators." The first of these devices was not built until 1932, and, as evidenced in the photographs and diagrams on pages 159 through 167, they have become increasingly spectacular. Through such instrumentalities, scientists hope to learn, for instance, the kinds of forces that operate within the nucleus, and the reactions that take place between the interacting particles.

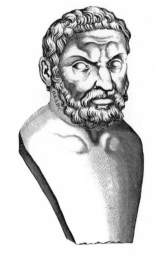

A WATERY VIEW OF MATTER
Thales of Miletus, a Greek of the Sixth Century B.C., theorized that all substances came from water and would eventually revert to water. This was man's first attempt to find some common denominator for the perplexing diversity of matter. Says one modern critic: "If he had championed . . . treacle . . . he would still have been rightly honored as the father of modern speculative science."

Already, by producing transmutations within the nucleus, they have identified 32 fundamental atomic particles, many of them unstable when born, often changing into other particles. But here, too, the more is known the more the mystery deepens. For physicists are no longer even sure that protons, neutrons and electrons do, in fact, "occupy space," as the dictionary definition of matter puts it. Some theories, in fact, describe these particles as waves, or points without volume—to quote one physicist, "mathematical singularities *haunting* space."

It begins to appear that the question of what *is* matter can probably not be answered—at least at present—in an ultimate, unchanging way.

Man's organized inquisitiveness about matter—gauged by the millennia of his sojourn on earth—is relatively recent. Yet as in all human effort, each era of his manipulation of matter has drawn on the one preceding. Modern chemistry owes a debt to the investigative zeal and laboratory techniques of medieval alchemy. The principles of alchemy stemmed from a theory by Aristotle about the "four elements" of the universe. The Greeks' philosophical musings about matter, including an atomic theory with strikingly modern aspects, were based on observations of the workings of the rudimentary chemistry handed down by the Babylonians and Egyptians. And their skills grew out of the cruder crafts of primitive trail blazers.

Sticks, stones and progress

Prehistoric man himself learned about matter only by trial, error and accident. His initial encounters with it came in choosing between poisonous and palatable plants; in finding that sticks rubbed together produced fire; in fashioning flints and other hard stones into crude tools. His next big strides forward came with his discovery of metals. Gold may have been the earliest to catch his notice, in the alluvial sands washed down from its places of origin; he may have seen his first glint of copper in a fire banked with earth containing its ore. Somehow tin got smelted in his fires, and he found that tin and copper together produced bronze. Next was iron, which probably first drew his eye in the form of meteorite fragments from outer space. Learning to work these metals launched him on the science of matter we now call metallurgy. And beyond metals, he became aware of other materials: colored minerals which would brighten the walls of his cave, and glassy matter, which he may have spotted first in obsidian, a semitransparent substance found in the residue of volcanic eruptions. Quartz crystal tools have been found with the bones of Peking man who inhabited the earth about a million years ago.

All these fortuities of matter prehistoric man was content merely to accept. It remained for his heirs in the budding civilizations of the Near East to perceive that matter could be changed. A Babylonian clay tablet

AN ERRONEOUS THEORY THAT LASTED 2,000 YEARS

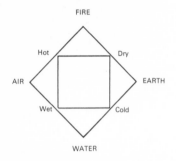

A FOURFOLD SYMMETRY

The illustrations on these pages show three versions—over a period of 2,000 years—of Aristotle's classic and incorrect theory that all matter was made of four elements: fire, air, water and earth. Each of these in turn was supposed to possess two of four basic properties: hot, cold, wet and dry. As the diagram above shows, Aristotle believed dry and cold united to form earth; cold and wet, water; wet and hot, air; hot and dry, fire. Formulated in the Fourth Century B.C., the theory was embraced by alchemists and philosophers alike, and dominated and delayed the progress of science until the 17th Century.

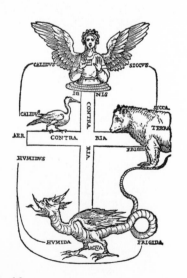

DRAGON, ANGEL, BIRD AND BEAST

Aristotle's four elements were often personified by living creatures, as in this drawing *(left)* from the *Pretiosa Margarita Novella,* an alchemical encyclopedia published in Venice in 1546. The dragon represents water, the angel fire, the bird air and the beast earth. The Latin names correspond to the English names on the geometrical diagram above. The Latin *Contraria* written in the crosses signifies the belief that air was opposed to earth and fire opposed to water.

of 6000 B.C. depicts the preparation of a crude beer for sacrificial purposes; Egyptian hieroglyphs of 3400 B.C. show wine presses. The early makers of wine and beer may not have been able to explain fermentation and its dependence on yeast, a one-celled fungus in the air and on ripe fruits, but they were aware that some transformation occurred. They learned, too, how to melt sodium minerals into glass; by 4000 B.C. the predynastic Egyptians were making decorative beads and jars by putting glazes on pieces of stone or quartz. By then they had also learned the art of dyeing, drawing on earlier knowledge that certain insects and berries would stain the fingers. Red dye came from the intestines of the insect *kermes* (hence crimson); blue dye from the indigo plant. By 1500 B.C. the citizens of Tyre in ancient Phoenicia knew that the gland of a shellfish, murex, turned yellow when exposed to air, then bright blue, finally purple; Tyrian purple became the badge of royalty. Then some unsung genius found that alum, a whitish mineral substance, would help "fix" the dye on a cloth immersed in it. Applying such fixatives to various portions of the same cloth in a single dye bath could produce a coat of many colors.

The worth of weight

Because man in those days was unaware of the deeper meaning of his accomplishments, later generations have denigrated his role in advancing our knowledge of matter; but it was no less vital than that of the laboratory miracle workers of today. In all these early transformations of matter, many of the rudiments of chemistry were established: the formation of insoluble compounds in dyeing, the typical biochemical process of fermentation, the reduction of ores by high-temperature techniques. And in the ancient marketplaces still another fundamental aspect of matter—indeed its most concrete value to date—manifested itself. As trade flourished, the *weight* of matter took on import. Systems of weights and measures became imperative; the Babylonians, for example, devised a shekel weighing about a third of an ounce and a talent weighing about 67 pounds. But history does not indicate that they reflected on the reasons for the weight of matter, or for its size, volume or density.

The first people to stop taking matter for granted were the Greeks. Hungry for knowledge, irrepressibly curious, they journeyed far afield, visiting Near Eastern centers of learning and reaping a rich harvest, including much information about the practical chemistry routinely employed in that part of the world. Then, through deduction and debate—they were probably the greatest talkers in history—the Greeks proceeded to work up an imposing body of theory about matter.

The first to weigh in with his ideas was the philosopher Thales of Miletus, six centuries before Christ. Wondering about the *physis* (nature) of matter and its properties, he sought—as men still do—for an

FROM CHEMISTRY TO ALLEGORY

The engravings below, by the Flemish artist Crispijn van de Passe (1564-1637), show allegorical figures in decorative scenes symbolizing Aristotle's four elements. Fire *(ignis)* holds brands and a burning coal. Water *(aqua)* wields a flowing pitcher while behind her a fisherman plies his trade. Earth *(terra)* carries a cornucopia of the earth's fruits while a hunter pursues its beasts. Air *(aer)* strides across the clouds, birds flying around him, the four winds blowing.

answer that was all-embracing. His final judgment was that the basic stuff of the universe was water. Thales had good reason to think so. Of all things within his grasp and vision, water was the most changeable—liquid in its natural state, becoming a solid as ice, or turning into vapor on a hot summer day.

Anaximenes, a contemporary of Thales, developed another theory simply by blowing air from his mouth onto his hand. If he blew with his mouth wide open, the air felt hot; if he blew with his mouth almost closed, the air felt cool. He concluded that heat was produced by the swift escape of air, and cooling by its constriction behind tight lips. He had it exactly backward, as anyone well knows who has pumped a tire or let air from it. But from his observations of the way breath, which is vital to human life, can be compressed and expanded, Anaximenes concluded that air—imbuing all nature with its ever-changing characteristics, permeating everything—was the basic stuff of the universe.

In the Fifth Century B.C. a Greek named Heraclitus put forth the idea that fire was the basic constituent of matter. Fire was forever changing; a flame grew or flickered or died down, yet it was always fire. In this ceaseless change and ceaseless sameness, Heraclitus believed, matter revealed its essential unity.

Love, hate and a theory

To water, air and fire, Empedocles, a Greek from the Sicilian colonies, added earth, combining all into a theory of four "elements," or roots. These, he argued, united before a force called love and disunited before a force called strife or hatred. The Empedoclean theory made a certain amount of sense. Earth, water and air do represent the three common states of matter—solid, liquid and gas—and fire is indeed energy, the agency through which matter changes from one form to another.

Of all the Greek ideas of matter, however, the most arresting, in retrospect, was propounded by a philosopher named Leucippus, and later by his student Democritus. Matter, they said, was simply a concentration of tiny particles, or "atoms," so small that they could not be cut any further (the Greek word *atoma* means indivisible). Democritus held that atoms were in constant motion, that they combined with others in various ways, and that they differed from each other only in shape and in arrangement. Uncanny as it now seems, this excellent atomic theory was little more than a wild speculation, like dozens of others put forth any afternoon in the Athenian forum. Yet Democritus was headed in the right direction, even though he would not have dared to dream that his indivisible atom would some day be shattered into smaller bits.

Democritus was destined not only to be 24 centuries ahead of his time but also to be deprived of contemporary acclaim. When Aristotle came

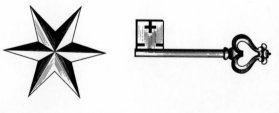

COPPER   COMMON SALT

along shortly thereafter to become the leading man of the hour, he not only failed to endorse the theory but bitterly attacked it—thereby, some historians feel, thwarting the development of modern atomic theory for an inexcusable span. Instead Aristotle conferred his favor upon the Empedoclean theory and, indeed, embellished it. In the Aristotelian version, the basis of the material world was a primitive matter which, however, existed only potentially until given form. Form gave rise to the "four elements," distinguished from one another by their qualities: hot, cold, dry and wet. None of the four elements, Aristotle theorized, was unchangeable; one might pass into another through the medium of the quality they possessed in common. Only the form changed; the prime matter composing the elements never changed.

An endowment from Aristotle

When darkness descended upon Greek culture, it was this Aristotelian concept which formed the philosophical basis of the next great advance in the science of matter—alchemy. From Aristotle's assumptions, the alchemists deduced their own postulates about the unity of matter and the existence of a transmuting agent, called the Philosopher's Stone, which—if produced—could turn base metals into gold and also become man's perfect medicine, the *elixir vitae*, or elixir of life.

Where and when the strange and often suspect art of alchemy arose is not known. Its practitioners thrived in both East and West. Within two centuries after Christ, one Wei Po Yang wrote the first Chinese tract on the preparation of an elixir which he labeled the "pill of immortality." The first Western alchemists were Alexandrian Greeks of about the same era. The word alchemy itself is derived from the Arabic, *alkimia*, in which *al* is the definite article and *kimia* is believed to come either from the Greek, *chyma*, meaning to fuse or cast a metal, or from *chem*, "the dark land"—the ancient Egyptians' name for their country.

Some of alchemy's charlatanries and achievements are pictured on the pages immediately following. As for its Aristotelian philosophical base, that was modified in time by a "doctrine of the two contraries." The contraries, or opposing elements, were sulphur, representing fire, or the quality of combustibility, and mercury, representing water, or the quality of fusibility or liquidity. These two qualities were believed to come into contact deep in the bowels of the earth and—depending on their proportions and their degree of purity—to produce base metals like lead or noble ones like silver and gold.

But although we have come to think of alchemy as no more than a fool's quest, its fundamental principle—that all kinds of matter had a common origin, that they possessed one permanent "soul" housed in a variety of temporary bodies, and that these bodies could be transmuted

SALTPETER   MERCURY   SAL AMMONIAC

ALCHEMY'S PICTURESQUE CODE
Since their consuming ambition was to turn cheap metals into gold, alchemists naturally evolved into a tight little ingroup which hid its formulas from the uninitiated —as well as from each other—by writing them in cryptic symbols like the ones at left. In one of these codes, the star signified copper; the key, common salt; the crescent and crown, saltpeter; the fish, mercury; the sun, sal ammoniac.

from one to another—bears a resemblance to the concept of unity of matter held in physics today.

Science, in fact, is not without some obligation to alchemy. In the attempt to prove their beliefs, the alchemists examined and tested virtually every substance known to man, thereby uncovering a good deal of the basic knowledge of the properties of various chemicals and compounds. Francis Bacon, the brilliant 16th Century Englishman who pioneered in the scientific method, gave one of the shrewdest summaries of alchemy's contribution to science:

"Alchemy may be compared to the man who told his sons that he had left them gold buried somewhere in his vineyard; where they by digging found no gold, but by turning up the mould about the roots of the vines, procured a plentiful vintage. So the search and endeavours to make gold have brought many useful inventions and instructive experiments to light."

Indeed, the alchemists were not entirely off the mark. Today we know that lead basically differs from gold in having 82 protons in its nucleus to gold's 79. It must then be possible to turn lead into gold by altering the nucleus. Modern science has provided us with the means to achieve "alchemical" transmutations, for within the huge particle accelerators the atomic constituents of matter can now be rearranged without destroying the basic unity of matter.

Alchemy's Pursuit of the Meaning of Matter

Man has always been intrigued by the stuff the world is made of, and never has he pursued this mystery more picturesquely than in the age of alchemy, that strange liaison of science and sorcery which flourished well beyond the Middle Ages and foreshadowed modern chemistry. Forever experimenting, ceaselessly pondering the nature of matter, the alchemist sometimes visualized his concepts in drawings like the bizarre three-armed dragon on the opposite page. But while his speculations often carried him into the realm of the murky and metaphysical, his laboratory goals were clear and concrete: to turn base metals into gold and to find the "elixir of life" that would make man immortal. Not surprisingly, alchemy had its charlatans. But its finest practitioners were dedicated investigators of nature, and scientists of any era would endorse the alchemical prayer: "Purge the horrible darknesses of our mind, light a light for our senses."

A MONSTER OF A THEORY
The page opposite, from *The Crowne of Nature,* a 16th Century book by an unknown Englishman, depicts a creature supposedly representing the "essence of mercury," which alchemists believed to be the most basic ingredient of all matter. The beast's three arms brandish *(left to right)* the alchemical symbols for silver, gold and mercury. Below them is the head of a bearded alchemist.

I which is the greene Lyon devouringe the ☉ is cold and moyst and is agrist flyinge from fire, and is the water of life when hee is once tinctured then doth hee tincture himselfe and other thinges also, and againe when hee is dissolued hee doth dissolue others also, and comminuted same instantly that it may be seene by the eyes sight, and successiuly it doth redone and hee is congregatinge or gatheringe water and the milke, and the strong drinke or piss and the mollifyinge ... and in a word the Father of all miracles and the servant runninge away, and the orientall I ... prefer himselfe aboue goulde and did outcome the same therfore the goulde said vnto it, what dost prefer thyselfe aboue me? I am the master of all stones experting or gouldinge out against the ... and vppon the I answered vnto it yet I doe preferring selfe about thee, for I haue brought ... and generated thee, and on part of my will or ran diuisify many parts of thee and I am the noble ... and in me the Science is hidden

Three in one.

The Correction of Fooles Fol. 7
Chap 6

The Philosopher sulpher is not to be vppon earth fownd but in those boddys ☉ and ☾ and some in certaine other boddy which knows none vnless it be riviall shewd him by God himselfe but in the ☉ it is most perfect because it is ... were digested and decocted.

EASTERN ELIXIR
This modern Oriental print *(left)* shows the alchemist Sun Po working his magic in the open air some 2,000 years ago. Sun Po allegedly made trees burst into flame, healed the sick by saying "Be whole!" and concocted an elixir of life. After this tour de force he disappeared.

WESTERN BONANZA
In this 17th Century Flemish painting *(above)* by David Teniers the Younger, an alchemist stirs a crucible while directing his helper to stoke the fire. The master's fur-trimmed cap is the hallmark of an "adept," one who claimed success in transmuting base metals into gold.

A FAVORABLE SKY FOR ALCHEMY
Alchemists often invoked astrology, as depicted in the Arabic text at left. The planet Mars, symbolized here by the war god, rides a ram (Aries) and wields a scorpion (Scorpio). These were supposed good omens for the process represented by the still at the animal's rear.

A Worldwide Lust for Everlasting Life and Lucre

Alchemy found its way into every corner of the civilized world—from the hills of China to European laboratories like the one above. The first Western alchemists were Alexandrian Greeks who thought that metals could be directly transmuted into gold, but most later Europeans believed no one could transmute anything until he had formulated the "Philosopher's Stone." There were many theories about the nature of this substance—whether actual stone, a tincture or a powder. But the main theory on how to use it was to encase it in wax and drop it into the molten metal that was being treated.

Some European alchemists also spent time searching for the elixir of everlasting life, an idea that probably came from Chinese alchemy *(opposite, top)* via Islamic texts *(opposite)*. Chinese alchemists were reputed to have created gold and the life-preserving potion as well. One of them wrote: "When the golden powder enters the five entrails, a fog is dispelled, like rainclouds scattered by wind. . . . The old dotard is again a lusty youth. . . ."

Arcane
Realms of Symbols
and Allegory

Alchemists habitually cloaked themselves in mystery to hide their secrets from the uninitiated. But to pass their knowledge along to their chosen disciples, they wrote many books rich in allegorical and symbolical illustrations, some of which appear on these pages. A base metal was often symbolized by a toad, a dragon or a human being. The essence of this metal was often depicted as a white bird. In the alchemists' credo, such symbolism linked the animate and inanimate. They believed that chemical change could be shown in terms of human change; that a union of two chemicals was like a human marriage; that turning base metals into gold was in some mystical way related to turning man's nature into something pure, noble and shining. The alchemists' search for the elixir of life also had other meanings: at one level it meant a quest for a perfect medicine; at another, it symbolized a desire for the realization of the whole man—man's attempt to perfect himself.

PLIGHT OF A KING
The painting at left, from an English manuscript of 1582, depicts the metal mercury as a king who is being boiled alive to produce his vapor, or soul, symbolized by the white bird about to fly from the king's head. An accompanying written parable implies that rejuvenation comes from being cut in pieces and boiled down, thereby engendering a renewal of strength and life.

WEALTH IN A FLASK

In the above illustration from the famed "Ripley Scrowle," an account of the work of the English alchemist George Ripley, the red object in the center is the Philosopher's Stone. Ripley claimed that this Stone could be made, in seven steps, from the substance represented by the tiny human in the flask: "First Calcine, and after that Putrefye, Dyssolve, Dystill, Sublyme, Descende, and Fyxe. . . ." However dubious his claims, Ripley's alchemical feats reputedly earned him enough to make him a £100,000-a-year donor to the Knights of St. John of Jerusalem.

FLIGHT OF A DOVE

These drawings, like the monster on page 17, are from *The Crowne of Nature*. The top flask illustrates the belief that when a metal is heated its spirit, symbolized by a dove, erupts from the charred body. Put into solution, the blackened metal is symbolized by a toad *(middle)*. The dove going back into solution *(bottom)* heralds the birth of a nobler substance, hopefully gold.

Home Brews and Hopeful Amateurs

Many alchemists were nobly motivated men of learning; many others were get-rich-quick schemers—like the rapt group shown here—who turned their homes into do-it-yourself laboratories and drove their families into poverty with their greedy compulsion to synthesize gold. This disorganized scene is full of typical alchemical apparatus: crucibles, pans, pots, tubs, jugs, flasks, pestles, mortars, stills, filters, a sieve, a basket of charcoal, drug jars, hand bellows, tongs, a trowel, a furnace for boiling water, and an hourglass and scales. All kinds of matter, curious and commonplace, found their way into the alchemists' seething crucibles—toads, urine, metals, animals, vegetables, minerals. Bernard of Treves once used over 2,000 hen's eggs in a single experiment. Another time he spent three years on a single experiment.

The untutored alchemists were often called "puffers" because they kept their bellows puffing night and day. The puffer in Chaucer's "Canon's Yeoman's Tale" offered one of the sharpest indictments ever made of the whole craft. His warning to every would-be alchemist: "If you would publish your infatuation / Come on and try your hand at transmutation; / If one of you has money in his fist / Step up and make yourself an alchemist. / Perhaps you think the trade is easily learnt? / Why then, come on and get your fingers burnt. . . ."

THE WAGES OF AVARICE
This engraving, from a 1558 pencil sketch by Pieter Bruegel the Elder, shows what happened when a poor amateur took a fling at alchemy. As he seeds a mixture with his last gold coin (one theory: it took gold to make gold), his wife bewails her empty purse and his children rummage in the foodless cupboard. His clerk reads the recipe; his puffer fans the fire. The inset *(upper right)* shows where Bruegel felt all this folly would lead: to the poorhouse.

In the 16th Century German engraving shown below, a progressive physician consults an alchemist for a remedy. Most doctors of the time were skeptical about the curative powers of alchemical potions, deeming them quack panaceas.

In Secret Formulas, New Skills for Old Trades

The following recipe was found in a manuscript attributed to the 13th Century alchemist Roger Bacon: "Of saltpetre take 7 parts, 5 of young hazel twigs, and 5 of sulfur; and so thou wilt call up thunder and destruction if thou know the art." Even today, the recipe still gives gunpowder.

Breaking their professional habit of playing things close to the vest, many alchemists in the centuries after Bacon exchanged know-how with other craftsmen —apothecaries, physicians, metallurgists. As shown in the engravings on the opposite page, alchemists gave to metallurgy furnaces and other apparatus for refining and alloying metals. With their knowledge of inorganic acids and salts as well as of traditional herb cures, many became apothecaries themselves. And physicians, long accustomed to preparing their own drugs, gradually began to consult alchemists about prescriptions *(left)*—the start of the modern doctor-druggist relationship.

THE MAGICAL MANDRAKE ROOT
From their scarecrow shape, mandrake roots *(right)* were often depicted as human, as in the 16th Century German engraving above. Fearing them but prizing their narcotic effect, alchemists rooted them up with dogs in dead of night.

THE TOOLS OF THE SMELTER

One of the many trades that drew on alchemy was metalworking. The scene at left shows what a two-man copper "factory" looked like in 16th Century Europe. Closely resembling an alchemy laboratory, it actually used equipment and techniques perfected by alchemists. A is a small smelting oven where copper ore was tested, B is the furnace door, C is the crushed ore, D is another testing oven, E is a bellows, F is a spherical water tank, G is a pot for melting copper with other metals to make alloys and H is a testing crucible. This engraving—as well as the others on this page—is from Lazarus Ercker's book on metallurgy published in Prague in 1574, a definitive work in its field for 200 years.

THE GOLD AMID THE SILVER

The alchemical equipment at right was used by early metallurgists to find the gold content of silver: A is an assay oven, B an iron tray, C a facial protector for looking into the oven, D a flask. E shows the metallurgist weighing silver.

THE TEST OF THE TOUCHSTONE

Metallurgy bequeathed to alchemy a variety of black quartz *(above)* popularly called a "touchstone." Rubbing the quartz with a sample of gold produces a yellow streak whose color and consistency reveal the impurities in the gold.

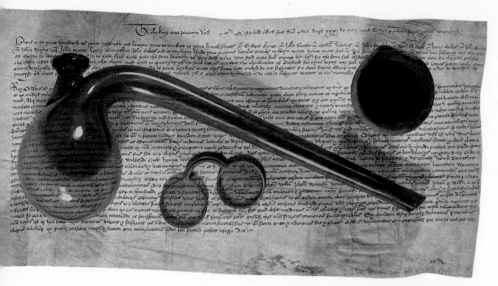

RELICS OF A FORBIDDEN CRAFT
A petition of 1457, sent to Henry VI of England by 12 alchemists seeking exemption from the law banning their practice, is shown in this photograph from the Museum of the History of Science at Oxford. The alchemist's glass retort, mortar and spectacles are also of English origin.

The Legacy of the Laboratory

For all their mumbo jumbo about three-armed dragons and parboiled kings, alchemists left behind a proud record of achievement. They are credited with the discovery of five elements—antimony, arsenic, bismuth, phosphorus and zinc—as well as alcohol and many of the acids and alkalies found in today's laboratories. They perfected such basic chemical procedures as distillation, crystallization, and the smelting and alloying of metals. But modern chemistry's greatest debt to its colorful ancestor is the idea and reality of the laboratory itself—with its experimental approach and its ingenious tools that were able to take matter apart and put it back together again. Much of this old equipment still survives in European museums. Some of these relics are shown in the photographs on these two pages.

Alchemy never achieved its ambition of changing one element into another, and smug Victorian scientists laughed at the goal itself. But modern nuclear physicists found a dramatic version of the elusive Philosopher's Stone in the neutrons that started the chain reaction which set off the first atomic bomb and transmuted uranium into some three dozen different chemical elements. The crafty old alchemists may have had the last laugh after all.

BASIC TOOLS FOR TRANSMUTATION
Some 17th and 18th Century alchemical equipment preserved at Oxford *(left)* includes a "Moor's Head" still. To the right *(bottom to top)*: a crucible, a retort, a clay vessel. To the left *(bottom to top)*: a bronze mortar, an alembic for distilling, an aludel for condensing vapors.

A SCENT OF THE PAST
Poland's University of Cracow, one of the oldest in Europe, has re-created a medieval workroom *(opposite)* with the décor of the 1490s—the time Copernicus was an undergraduate. Exuding an air of alchemy with its flasks, stuffed animals and zodiac disc with burning dragon, this restoration seeks to capture the mood and some trappings of an alchemist's laboratory.

The Basic Ingredients of a Complex World

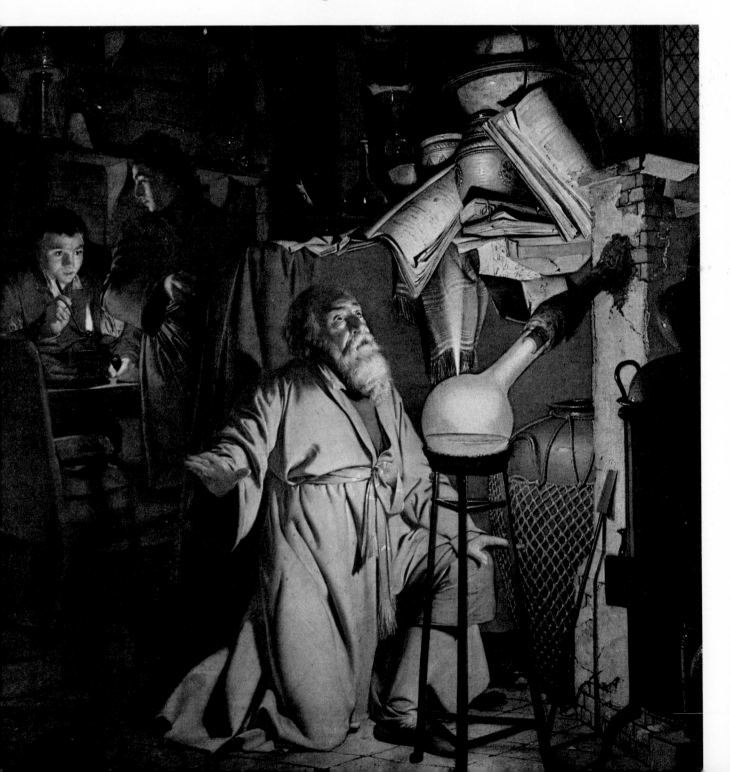

EVEN THE most modest householder among us, were he to count all the separate and distinct objects in his possession, would easily reach a final figure in the thousands. Were this inventory to be worldwide, and to include the contents of factories, farms and other centers of human enterprise, the number would total billions. Such is the fruit of man's ingenuity; the more civilized he has become, the more he has filled—some say cluttered—his existence with all manner of what he deems to be essentials, amenities and luxuries. Yet the extraordinary fact is that these myriads of objects—however dissimilar in shape, look or purpose—are made up, in one compound or another, of only 88 natural elements: substances, that is, peculiar unto themselves and not chemically reducible to a more basic constituent.

This limited larder of materials has produced the infinite variety of things by which man lives in much the same way a 26-letter alphabet has provided the enormous array of words by which he communicates: through differing combinations, arrangements and juxtapositions. Just as, for instance, the letters *a*, *e* and *r* make up the words *are*, *era*, *ear*, *area* and *rear*, so the elements carbon, hydrogen and oxygen appear in a pad of paper, a rubber eraser, a blob of glue, a paste of laundry starch, a lump of sugar and a dry Martini.

Elements fall into three categories: metals, which predominate (comprising three fourths of the total), nonmetals, and metalloids, which have some characteristics of both (arsenic, for example). Under ordinary conditions some elements, such as chlorine and neon, are gaseous; two, mercury and bromine, are liquid; most are solids, ranging from relative newcomers like hafnium and lutetium to old-timers like tin and iron.

Beside the 88 natural elements are 15 more, labeled "artificial." Some have been made in the laboratory, some through the decay of natural elements which are radioactive. Most of these artificial substances rapidly transform themselves into other substances and are extremely short-lived; many have never been produced in amounts large enough to be seen by the naked eye.

Whether artificial or natural, elements are grouped into "families," their hallmark being the way they behave when introduced to members of other families. The most high-hat are the "noble" gases, so called because they stay aristocratically aloof from all other elements. Two much more democratic clans are the halogens, or salt-formers, and the alkali metals; both readily associate with other elements. As to how many element families there are in all, scientists differ. Some count only eight, others—using more precise breakdowns of an element's behavior—count 18 (these have sat for their family portraits on pages 127 through 149).

Although the elements have, of course, been with us since the beginning, man has come to know them as such only in the past 300 years.

LIGHT IN ALCHEMY'S DARKNESS
The scene opposite, painted by the Englishman Joseph Wright in 1771, portrays the German alchemist Hennig Brand praying after his discovery in 1669 of a strange new element. His dark laboratory is lighted here by the eerie glow of his new find: phosphorus. Alchemists are thought to have identified at least four other elements: bismuth, arsenic, zinc and antimony.

Until then they were not recognized for what they were because they rarely appear in nature except in combination with each other, in chemical compounds which bear no physical resemblance to their progenitors.

Even when they cropped up in primitive times, elements did not pique man's curiosity; he was concerned not with what they were, but what they could do for him. As noted in the preceding chapter, he had a working acquaintance with gold, tin, copper and iron. He also knew carbon, formed as carbon black from soot. Later he came upon silver and lead. Experience taught him their traits and tricks: that gold and copper were wonderfully malleable; that copper and tin together produced an alloy (mixture) of superior strength, bronze; that iron could be hammered into shape when repeatedly heated and hardened into crude steel when the carbon of a charcoal fire was added. But in all this gradual accrual of know-how, early man failed to question the basic nature of the elements.

The Greeks and Romans, despite their higher civilization, did little better in this regard. The Parthenon, that enduring monument to Greek glory, was built with revenues from the Laurion lead mines. Some of the great Roman aqueducts in Spain were built to help process valuable tin deposits. By the time of Caesar's legions at their most far-flung, nine elements had been produced in fairly pure form, still without investigation of their underlying principle. What stalled this inquiry, beyond all else, was the persistence of the neatly packaged Aristotelian theory, mentioned earlier in these pages, that there were only "four elements" in the universe—earth, air, water and fire. In later centuries the alchemists clung to Aristotle's notion, even while adding arsenic, antimony, bismuth, phosphorus and zinc to man's storehouse of elements.

A skeptical seventh son

It remained for the self-taught master of science, the Anglo-Irishman Robert Boyle, the seventh son of the Earl of Cork, to lay down the fundamental principle of elements, in a book, *The Sceptical Chymist*, published in 1661: "I mean by elements . . . certain Primitive and Simple or perfectly unmingled bodies; which not being made of any other bodies, or of one another, are the Ingredients of which all those call'd perfectly mixt Bodies are immediately compounded, and into which they are ultimately resolved."

The man who dealt the death blow to the four-element theory was a kind of cross-Channel answer to Europe's Renaissance man. Boyle was a prolific writer, theologian, student of the sacred languages of the East, traveler, financier of the publication of Isaac Newton's *Principia*, chemist and physicist. Above all, he was a pioneer practitioner of the so-called "scientific method" which heralded the start of modern science. (The word scientist, itself based on the Latin *scire*, to know or learn, dates only from 1840.)

More properly, perhaps, "the scientific method" should be called "the scientific spirit." Its antithesis is the sort of closed philosophical system which caused the Church to forbid the great Galileo to argue that the earth moves around the sun. Its wellspring is the sort of unswerving dedication to truth which, the story goes, caused Galileo to mutter during his inquisition, "Nevertheless, it does move." Dedication—and curiosity—are certainly the prime ingredients of the scientific spirit; so are open-mindedness and a skepticism which refuses to accept as truth anything which cannot be demonstrated. Often, the spirit shows in a leaping intuition so uncanny and inexplicable as to seem paranormal, yet also in a plodding thoroughness at recording and classifying facts.

A fruitful merger of rivals

The effort has sometimes been made to set up a rivalry of scientific methods put forth shortly before Boyle's time by the Englishman Francis Bacon, who preached the patient accumulation of facts, and the Frenchman, René Descartes, who liked to propound grand concepts and stimulate the search for facts to prove them right. Using Bacon's method, the scientist collects, tabulates and compares as many instances as possible of the effect he is investigating, only then seeking to generalize; this is *induction*. Under Descartes' procedure, the scientist proceeds from some theory to the experiments which will prove or disprove it; this is *deduction*. Actually, the major advances in scientific thought have resulted from sometimes the first, sometimes the second method. And some of the very biggest have resulted from flashes of sheer inspiration which defy explanation. Einstein himself believed that there are times when logic can carry the mind no farther; and that thought then makes an intuitive leap whose origins are not clear to the thinker himself.

Back in the 17th Century, Robert Boyle applied the Baconian method in endless, exhaustive experiments to which science owes its first systematic knowledge of many elements and compounds. In those times there were no established criteria for chemical analysis. Color was not always a reliable guide. Two otherwise similar substances might have different colors because of impurities, yet in other cases different colors might be highly significant—for example, green, blue and white vitriol turn out to be, respectively, sulphates of iron, copper and zinc. Boyle, by the "flame test," showed how even a tiny bit of an element will show its presence by the distinctive color it gives to a flame.

Boyle's tireless experimenting, recording and classifying made it possible to identify substances of many kinds with a certainty previously known only for some metals. He himself played a key role in unfolding

"DOCTOR PHLOGISTON"
The words above were the original caption on this 18th Century cartoon mocking the English clergyman-scientist Joseph Priestley for his radical ideas on politics and religion and his defense of the antiquated theory which held that fire was merely the freeing of a mysterious element called phlogiston. Almost lynched for supporting the French Revolution, Priestley came to America to continue his work isolating gases. He also invented soda water.

the identity of the first element positively known to have been isolated by a single individual: white phosphorus. This feat, in turn—a milestone in the understanding of matter—was unwittingly achieved by a German alchemist, Hennig Brand. Like others of his craft, Brand was perpetually in pursuit of that purported be-all and end-all of substances, the Philosopher's Stone. One day in 1669, in his laboratory in Hamburg, he fired up his furnace, filled a retort with a certain liquid and evaporated it to see what sediments would result. What emerged was a pasty white substance. As dusk enveloped the room it began to glow; when Brand lifted a fragment of it from the remaining liquid, it burst into flame.

Brand showed off his strange new product but kept secret its liquid source until the information was wheedled from him, for a price, by one Johann Daniel Krafft of Dresden. Concocting his own supply of the magical substance, Krafft in time went to England to demonstrate this "perpetual fire" to King Charles II. There he met Boyle, who could elicit from him only the hint that the origin of the substance was "somewhat that belonged to the body of man." Experimenting, Boyle tracked down the mystery: he found the source to be urine. Ultimately, on his own, he rediscovered phosphorus.

For his accomplishments, Boyle is often hailed as the father of modern chemistry: at least as often, that honor is ascribed to a brilliant Frenchman of the following century, Antoine Laurent Lavoisier. Boyle laid down the basic definition of an element; Lavoisier laid down the basic standard for testing whether a substance fitted that definition: an element was "the last point which analysis is capable of reaching." With this as an operational guideline, impostors and impersonators among the elements could be winnowed out, and an accurate membership roster assembled. In 1789 a listing by Lavoisier included 23 elements as we know them today.

The demolition of a ghost

Lavoisier made another vital contribution by demolishing the so-called phlogiston theory, long dear to the scientific community. Advanced by a German, Georg Ernst Stahl, this notion propounded the existence, in all combustible substances and metals, of an invisible substance, phlogiston —a sort of handy, all-purpose ingredient which could be used to explain all manner of chemical reactions. Thus, for instance, the reason why a substance crumbled to ash when burned was that phlogiston had "departed" from it; the reason why a calx, or metallic oxide (a soft powder), resumed metallic form when heated with charcoal was that it "took up" phlogiston from the charcoal. While for decades scientists were content to accept the alleged all-embracing wonders of the ghostly phlogiston, a certain unease greeted the phlogistonists' assertion that, depending on

MOLECULAR BLUEPRINT, OLD AND NEW

Like many chemists before him, John Dalton devised a personal set of symbols for the known elements, five of which are shown below ("alumine" and "potash" were Dalton's names for aluminum and potassium). His attempt to draw the potassium aluminum sulphate molecule, ordinary alum, is shown at the bottom of the page alongside a corrected drawing of this compound.

 OXYGEN

 ALUMINUM (ALUMINE)

 SULPHUR

 POTASSIUM (POTASH)

 HYDROGEN

A RIGHT AND WRONG PICTURE

Shown at immediate right is Dalton's design for potassium aluminum sulphate, which he called "potash alum." If a chemist today were to use the same symbols, he would design the molecule like the one at far right. Except for its omission of hydrogen, Dalton's molecule contained all the correct elements; but he had them in the wrong proportions. This was partly because he had no way of determining the exact number of atoms in a compound and partly because he often confused compounds with elements.

DALTON'S MOLECULE

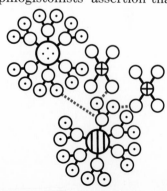

ACTUAL MOLECULE

the particular chemical occasion, phlogiston could have weight, or be weightless, or even exhibit what they called "negative" weight. It was over this issue that the theory ultimately foundered.

Using specially made balances more accurate than ever before employed—one of them could measure a weight change as small as a hundredth the weight of a drop of water—Lavoisier performed a classic series of experiments with precisely weighed quantities of tin and lead. In one of them he placed tin in a flask, sealed it, weighed it, heated it until no more of the powdery calx was formed and reweighed the flask: no weight change. Then he broke the seal, allowing air to rush in, and weighed the flask again. This time he found a weight increase.

History in a red powder

Lavoisier concluded that the increase was due to the weight of the air rushing in when the flask was unsealed—and that this weight had replaced the weight of air originally in the closed apparatus, which had been used up in forming the calx. Just what had been removed from this latter air in the process of combustion and calcination (calx-forming), Lavoisier was uncertain; he described it generally as some "atmospheric principle." In time he had the specific answer from a visiting English scientist-cleric, Joseph Priestley, who told him of an experiment of his own. Instead of forming a calx, Priestley had unformed one—powdery red mercuric oxide—by heating it with sunlight through a magnifying glass. In the process he had liberated a new gas which, as a confirmed phlogistonist, he had labeled "dephlogisticated air." Lavoisier, recovering this "air" in a new experiment, found it to be the "atmospheric principle" he had sought: the one responsible for both combustion and calcination—and indeed, further tests proved, for the respiration of all living things. Finding that it had acid-forming properties, he named it after the Greek for acid, *oxys*, with the suffix *gène*, for forming: oxygen.

Lavoisier went on to other experiments with other chemical reactions, out of which he formulated the principle that the total weight of the products of a reaction exactly equals the combined weight of the reactants from which they were formed; chemical change, in short, caused no loss of mass. With this finding, it was as if blinders had been lifted from the laboratory workers of the world: the ceaseless chemical interplay of the elements could be analyzed in depth.

Within a quarter century after Lavoisier, the elements, for the first time, were put on an organized footing. A specific weight (mass) was assigned to the atom of each element known, and quantitative relationships were shown to exist between elements. The man responsible for this monumental work was an English Quaker, John Dalton, who began life as a village schoolmaster and went on to become a professor of math-

ARCHITECT OF MATTER
Headmaster of a school at the age of 12, the English scientist John Dalton (1766-1844) is caricatured above as an old man holding a rain gauge. During his lifetime he recorded daily weather statistics 200,000 times, but his real fame rests on having unearthed the ancient belief of Democritus that all matter was built up from tiny indestructible particles called atoms. Dalton gave the theory flesh and bones by preparing the first table of atomic weights —and was the first to sketch the structure of many chemical compounds *(opposite)*.

ematics and natural philosophy at the University of Manchester. (He died a bachelor, never having had "time to marry." This dilemma was perhaps partially explained by just one of his pursuits, the habit of daily jotting down in his diary his observations of weather conditions; the total of such notations came to 200,000.)

In 1808 Dalton enunciated the theory that in their smallest chemically acting parts, elements are composed of atoms which are immutable in chemical changes, and that all atoms of a given element weigh the same, but differ in weight from atoms of other elements. An atom's weight, therefore, was a characteristic of an element; a number representing that weight could be assigned to an element; and on this basis there could be an order in the scheme of the elements. In lieu of measuring the atom itself to try to determine its true weight, Dalton proposed that the lightest substance known, hydrogen, be arbitrarily assigned a weight of 1, and that the atoms of other elements be assigned weights relative to this standard. When water was split into its two elements—hydrogen and oxygen—it was found that the oxygen weighed seven times the hydrogen, a ratio of 1:7 (today the accepted value is about 1:8). On Dalton's primitive but portentous table of atomic weights, oxygen was then assigned the number 7; making other comparisons of this kind, he numbered nitrogen 5, carbon 5, phosphorus 9, sulphur 13. In some instances Dalton's weights were considerably off, but his introduction of the quantitative factor was a major advance; eventually atomic weights were correctly assessed.

A covey of combinations

Dalton also advanced the idea that chemical compounds are composed of atoms of elements combined in definite proportions. Carbonic oxide and carbonic acid, he found, would yield different proportions of oxygen when broken into their constituents: the oxide (carbon monoxide) had equal parts of carbon and oxygen, but the acid (carbon dioxide) had two parts of oxygen for each of carbon. This suggested that instead of combining with each other in fixed proportions, the same elements might combine in several multiples of one another to form a variety of quite different compounds. Finding many instances in which this occurred, he noted that the elements seemed to combine in simple arithmetical multiples—two to one, as in carbon dioxide, or three to one, or three to two.

Dalton concluded that the smallest portion of a compound consisted of a grouping of a definite number of atoms of each element—what he called a "compound atom," and what we now know as a "molecule." One puzzle, however, was *why* atoms combined in such different ways. Why, for instance, did hydrogen and oxygen form either water, only one atom of oxygen combining with two of hydrogen, or hydrogen peroxide, two atoms of oxygen combining with two of hydrogen? In time, this puzzle was solved by the concept of "valence," or "combining capacity."

The early concepts of valence assumed that each element's atom had one or more "hooks"—only one hook for hydrogen, two for an oxygen atom. Thus, oxygen could grasp a hydrogen hook in each of its two hooks, forming H_2O, water; or two oxygen atoms, linking one of their hooks, could each grab a hydrogen hook, forming H_2O_2, hydrogen peroxide. We now know that a variation of such grouping actually does occur. Indeed, *identical* numbers of atoms can produce *different* compounds, depending on how they group themselves—glucose and fructose, for example, are both composed of 6 carbon, 12 hydrogen and 6 oxygen atoms.

It should be noted that the now familiar symbols of the elements—C for carbon, H for hydrogen, O for oxygen, and so on—were not yet in use when Dalton held sway. To signify metals and other substances, the Greeks had used either contractions of their words for these materials or pictorial representations of the planets; similar motifs sufficed for the alchemists. In time the symbol situation bordered on chaos. One early 17th Century Italian manuscript designated mercury alone by no fewer than 20 symbols; another represented lead by 14. Dalton's orderly solution to the problem was a schematic system in which the atoms of various elements were represented by circles with lines and dots; various groupings of the circles designated his beloved "compound atoms." Some chemists found Dalton's symbolism clumsy, and the breakthrough to modern usage awaited a contemporary Swede, Jöns Jacob Berzelius; with only slight changes, his are the symbols of today. Berzelius discarded Dalton's ideographs and used either the initial letter, or some combination of the first few letters, of the Latin name for each element. Thus, for example, potassium became K (for *kalium*), silver became Ag (for *argentum*) and tin Sn (for *stannum*). Dalton clung to his own system; the Berzelius symbols, he insisted, were "horrifying."

Interest in symbolizing the elements, however, was secondary to interest in rooting them up. As new knowledge continued to come to light about the known elements, appetites were whetted for the unknown as well. Even by Dalton's day element-hunting had become a great scientific sport (uranium, so intimately linked with our own age, was discovered way back in 1789, by a German, Martin Klaproth). Throughout the first half of the 19th Century the tempo of the chase quickened; by 1870, a total of 65 elements had been captured and tagged.

It was a motley array in which little perceptible order reigned; interrelationships between elements, possible family ties, seemed to defy positive identification. What was required was a systematic, persistent, incredibly patient examination of great and often bewildering masses of fact. This mammoth task was undertaken by a Russian, Dmitri Mende-

THE PIONEER OF ELEMENTAL ORDER

DMITRI IVANOVICH MENDELEYEV
This Soviet stamp was issued in 1934, on the centennial of the birth of Dmitri Mendeleyev, the Russian chemist who discovered that a natural order existed among the elements. As shown below in a reproduction of his original chart, Mendeleyev arranged the elements according to their atomic weight, and then pointed out that elements side by side in adjacent columns (e.g., vanadium, niobium, tantalum) behaved in the same way. Gaps in the table—shown as question marks—never fazed Mendeleyev: he explained them with bold and accurate predictions about the chemical properties of undiscovered elements.

			Ti=50	Zr=90	?=180.
			V=51	Nb=94	Ta=182.
			Cr=52	Mo=96	W=186.
			Mn=55	Rh=104,4	Pt=197,4
			Fe=56	Ru=104,4	Ir=198.
			Ni=Co=59	Pl=106,6	Os=199.
H=1			Cu=63,4	Ag=108	Hg=200.
	Be=9,4	Mg=24	Zn=65,2	Cd=112	
	B=11	Al=27,4	?=68	Ur=116	Au=197?
	C=12	Si=28	?=70	Sn=118	
	N=14	P=31	As=75	Sb=122	Bi=210
	O=16	S=32	Se=79,4	Te=128?	
	F=19	Cl=35,5	Br=80	I=127	
Li=7	Na=23	K=39	Rb=85,4	Cs=133	Tl=204
		Ca=40	Sr=87,6	Ba=137	Pb=207.
		?=45	Ce=92		
		?Er=56	La=94		
		?Yt=60	Di=95		
		?In=75,6	Th=118?		

35

leyev, a leonine man of dauntless spirit. A glimpse inside any high-school science classroom today will attest to his triumph: hanging resplendent in color on the wall, the familiar Periodic Chart of Elements is—albeit in modern dress—his enduring handiwork.

When Mendeleyev began his magnum opus, in the late 1860's, he was not much over 30, but held the chair of general chemistry at the University of St. Petersburg—an eminence he had attained after a slow start. Siberian-born, youngest of 17 children, he had, at the age of 15, traveled the long road to Moscow by wagon, with his mother, to seek admission to the university there. Madame Mendeleyev considered her boy a scientific genius; the academic authorities did not. Rejected, Dmitri pushed on to St. Petersburg, where he entered the university's Pedagogical Institute. Although hampered in his youth by tuberculosis, he became a master teacher, chemist and adviser to the Russian oil industry. The esteem in which he was held was to be lifelong; in later years, when he took a second wife while not yet divorced from his first, the czar's reported comment was, "Mendeleyev has two wives, yes, but I have only one Mendeleyev."

The now classic periodic table grew out of Mendeleyev's preparations for his book, *Principles of Chemistry*, published in 1868. Contemplating his plan of approach, he was struck by the lack of systematization of the facts of inorganic chemistry. He set about collecting every bit of evidence about the nature of every known element, with the intent of seeing if there were any "periodic"—regular—order among them. Some data were already available. It was known, for instance, that the halogens, or salt-forming elements (fluorine, chlorine, bromine, iodine), had common characteristics. So did the alkali metals (including at the time lithium, sodium and potassium, and later to be augmented by rubidium, cesium and francium), which quickly oxidized on exposure to air and hence were never found naturally in other than a compound form. So did the "noble" metals (copper, silver and gold), so called because they were durable and corrosion-resistant.

A placement of pin-ups

On a wall in his laboratory Mendeleyev began a pin-up system for cataloguing his information. One oblong card was assigned per element; these cards he then arranged and rearranged on the wall. On each card he noted the atomic weight and other properties of the element and its compounds. Eventually he worked out a system of lateral rows and vertical columns into which he placed the cards to reflect chemical and physical similarities between groups of elements. Putting hydrogen in a special place because of its unique properties, he set down, in the first row, the next seven known elements from lithium to fluorine, in sequence of their increasing atomic weights. In the second row he wrote the next seven, from sodium to chlorine. In these two rows alone, the periodicity of chemical behavior was already obvious: in the first vertical column were the first two alkali metals, in the seventh were the first two halogens; and in each of the other vertical columns the elements were chemically similar.

It was the genius of Mendeleyev to see these relationships without knowing why they took place. When he began his third lateral row of seven elements, potassium fell into its proper place beneath lithium and sodium. Next came calcium, similar to magnesium and beryllium above it. For the third column, the next element known at that time was titanium. But Mendeleyev recognized that its properties were similar to those of carbon and silicon, which were in the *fourth* column, so he put titanium directly below them and *left the third place in the row blank*. To make the classification complete, there would have to be a hitherto unsuspected element whose atomic weight was between that of calcium (40) and titanium (48).

A prophecy in Sanskrit

Mendeleyev made the same courageous assumptions about other blank spaces among his pin-ups; sooner or later, he asserted, the missing elements would turn up. He even named these absent members, invoking the Sanskrit prefixes *eka* and *dvi* (for "one" and "two") in combination with the names of analogous known elements one or two places away in the periodic grouping. "It is possible," he wrote, "to foretell the properties of still unknown elements." This confident prediction was fulfilled, first, with the discovery of gallium in 1875; its properties almost precisely matched those of "eka-aluminum." His "eka-boron"—the missing element between calcium and titanium—was discovered in 1879 in Sweden and named scandium; his "eka-silicon" was found in Germany in 1886 and named germanium—one material of today's transistors. And although Mendeleyev did not anticipate the inert, or "noble," gases, when they came along during the later years of his life they were easily fitted into his chart, simply by the creation of a new vertical column.

For all his vision, Mendeleyev could not foresee that in a few decades after his death in 1907 the laboratories of the new century would be producing man-made elements to add to his historic chart. But as for the elements appearing in nature, the list is complete; it begins with the lightest gas, hydrogen, No. 1, and ends with the heaviest metal, uranium, No. 92. This latter number, in view of the existence of only 88 natural elements, would seem to indicate a discrepancy; it is, however, explained by four elements—technetium, promethium, astatine and francium—which are included among the first 92 by reason of their atom-

	1500s	1600s	1700s	1783	1808	1814
GOLD						Au
MERCURY						Hg
LEAD						Pb

AN EVOLVING CHEMICAL SHORTHAND
Shown at left is the evolution of the chemical symbols for three common metals. All derive from alchemy, which often depicted the sun as a symbol for gold, the caduceus of the god Mercury as the symbol for mercury, and the scythe of the god Saturn as the symbol for lead. Modern alphabetic notation introduced in 1814 by the Swedish chemist Jöns Berzelius gives these elements letter symbols based on their ancient names—aurum, hydrargyrum and plumbum.

ic weight, but either do not actually occur in nature or are produced for just an instant in the process of radioactive decay. We know now that no more natural elements will ever be discovered between hydrogen and uranium because of one simple fact. Just as an element has its atomic "weight," so it has an atomic "number" on the list, based on the quantity of protons in the nucleus of its atoms. It is hydrogen's single proton that makes it first on the list; each successive element has just *one* additional proton. There can be no further additions within the list because there is no such thing as a fractional proton.

If this knowledge has curbed man's adventurous searches for elements in the earth and air around him, other knowledge, perhaps, compensates. Astronomers using spectrographs coupled to their powerful telescopes have explored the structure of distant stars and have found that the universe as a whole is composed of the same elements which are grouped on Mendeleyev's chart. Stars billions of light-years remote in space send spectral messages which reveal that they, too, contain hydrogen, helium and the other elements well known on earth. Thus we can be certain that when we study matter on earth, we are working with the same substances of which the universe is composed. The stuff of the stars, to be sure, may exist under quite different conditions—compressed to incredible density or heated to many millions of degrees—but there, as here, the elements are the same.

Indispensable Interpreters of an Age of Science

Not the least startling fact of science today is the drastic change in the public image of its practitioners. A generation ago the chemist and the physicist were regarded as remote tinkerers. Nowadays the physical scientist is no more comprehensible to laymen—he talks of vector bosons and polymer viscoelasticity, and writes of "Spin Wave Equations in De-Sitter Space"—but for all this he now basks in popular acclaim. Vast resources of money and equipment lie at his disposal; government and industry hang on his word. The remarkable rise of the scientist has been due, beyond all else, to his successful probes of the structure and behavior of matter, and to his essential role as interpreter of the atomic age which he thereby helped launch. Yet one of the most incisive of these interpreters, J. Robert Oppenheimer *(opposite)*, says that one simple prerequisite is still most essential for a man who enters his field: "Mostly that he loves it."

ELDER STATESMAN OF PHYSICS
Chief architect of the first atomic bomb and a noted sparker of ideas among U.S. physicists, J. Robert Oppenheimer now directs Princeton's Institute for Advanced Study, headquarters for some of the world's most brilliant thinkers. "Physicists," says Oppenheimer, "combine acute curiosity with an acute need for order. . . . We'd like to understand what the devil matter is all about."

A PROBER OF PARTICLES

Jack Steinberger, 42, relaxes in a clutter of equipment in Columbia University's Nevis Laboratory at Irvington, New York. Early in his career, Steinberger tried theoretical physics, "but I found it very hard to have ideas." After that he switched to being an experimentalist, and he has since been engaged in extensive research on elementary particles—the basic constituents of matter. To be a scientist, Steinberger feels, "it doesn't hurt to be clever, and to be inventive." For him, the joy of work "is the freedom you have—you are free to do what you want."

A CHANGE OF OPINION

Leonard Reiffel, 35, stands outside the "hot room," where radioactive experiments are conducted at the I.I.T. (Illinois Institute of Technology) Research Institute in Chicago. As head of the institute's physics research division, Reiffel has a dual role—part researcher, part administrator. He directs 260 people at work on 50 projects, ranging from optics to outer space. "In my college days," Reiffel says, "I thought physicists were stodgy types doing abstract thinking in ivory towers, rutting around in their work. The Manhattan Project changed all that."

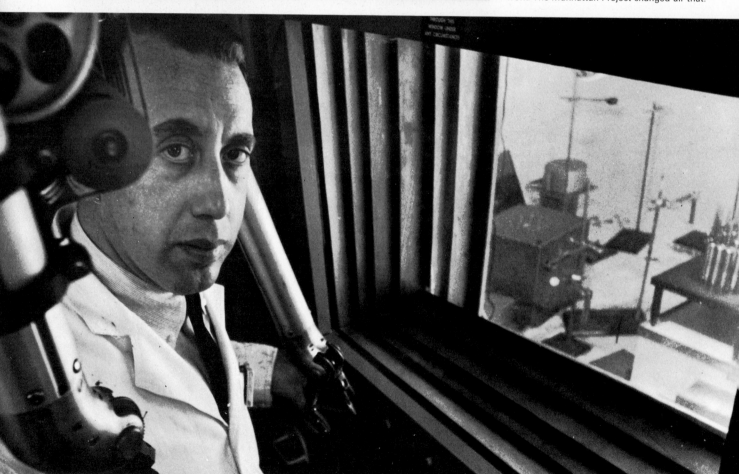

Habitats of the Select Fraternity Of Physicists

Of the current vintage crop of scientists, none stirs popular imagination more than the physicist. His usual habitat is either a government installation *(right)*, a university laboratory *(opposite)* or a foundation-sponsored research center *(lower left)*. But wherever he works, it is likely to be amid massive machines and costly facilities. Some physicists, however, remain aloof from all laboratories. These are the armchair—or blackboard—scientists: theoreticians who spin theses but leave the testing of them to the experimentalists (a new term for experimenters).

Some 32,000 physicists ply their profession in the U.S., ranging from the cryogenicists, who deep-freeze matter to almost absolute zero, to the plasma physicists *(pages 44-45)*, who handle matter at temperatures hotter than the sun. There are both the "pure" and the "applied" researchers, and they do not always communicate. "I haven't any notion of what goes on in industrial labs," says university physicist Jack Steinberger *(opposite)*.

A Ph.D. in physics requires at least three years of graduate study, of which at least one is in original research. On the average an American physicist earns $12,-000 a year (a few earn upward of $40,000). Like mathematicians, they often do their best work early in life, but unlike most mathematicians, physicists seem to continue their creative output to a ripe old age.

A MESS OF MESONS
Roger Hildebrand, 41, associate director of Chicago's Argonne National Laboratory, nuclear reactor design and technology center, looks up from the base of an atom-smashing synchrotron. An administrator, teacher and researcher, Hildebrand is personally intrigued with some subatomic particles called mu-mesons, which behave so oddly "they mess up all our calculations. We don't know why nature bothered to make them." But teaching also delights him: "I don't think my research would be nearly as good if I didn't have my students to keep me on the ball."

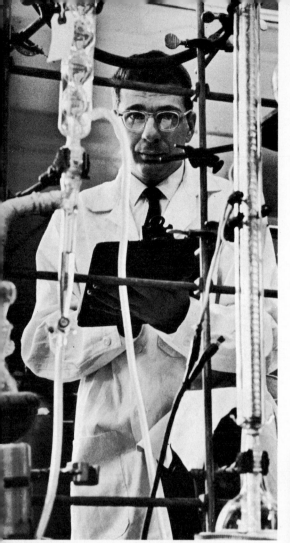

The Chemists: Men with Designs on Nature

The workshops of the modern chemist are as varied as those of the physicist; he too is courted by the government, universities, corporations and research foundations. While chemistry has been deemed less glamorous than physics, its practitioners view this fact philosophically. "Science tends to go in fads," remarks Robert Burns Woodward (below). Actually, few fields of science outshine biochemistry, which delves into the chemistry of life, the genetic code, viruses and cancer.

In recent years chemists have been fascinated by the problems of synthesis—the step-by-step tailor-making of large, even giant, molecules for specific purposes. To bend nature to new designs, chemists have had to probe the ultimate structure of matter. Research, both basic and applied, has produced a plethora of new plastics and foams, fibers and films, adhesives and de-

tergents—as well as synthetic hormones, countless new drugs and high-powered fuels. But not all chemists are synthesizers: among the 110,000 chemists in the U.S., some are in such practical specialties as chemical marketing and sewerage chemistry. Increasingly, chemistry merges with other disciplines: a scientist studying crystals may hardly know whether he is involved in structural chemistry or solid-state physics.

Like physicists, chemists are rigorously trained, earn about as much, and tend more and more to specialize. Such has been the explosive growth of the field that an individual can barely keep up with the technical reading required to keep abreast of even a narrow speciality, a burden noted by George Schmidt (left). "Much of a chemist's work," he says, "is reading and writing—too much of it, in fact."

BEYOND PURE THEORY
George Schmidt, 35, a polymer chemist with Allied Chemical Corporation, checks a special distillation apparatus in his laboratory. He specializes in the synthesis of new polymers, the huge molecules in plastics, fibers and other products which his firm may market. An applied experimentalist himself, Schmidt believes that to a greater or lesser degree all scientists have practical goals. "I don't believe there is such a thing as a pure theoretical scientist," he observes. "Even the most theoretical can project far into the future and see some practical consequence of his work. However, he is not so concerned with *how soon* his discoveries are converted into some beneficial product."

A BROAD VISTA
Robert Burns Woodward, 46, holder of nine honorary Doctor of Science degrees and one of the nation's leading synthetics chemists, peers at a sample of a substance which may lead to the laboratory production of vitamin B-12, one of several research projects he directs. In addition to synthesizing chlorophyll, quinine and cortisone, Woodward has helped revolutionize synthetic chemistry by insisting on a broad theoretical approach rather than the trial-and-error methods widespread in the past. Although he does not feel that chemistry and physics will ever really merge, Woodward notes that "chemists now are alert to the use of physical discoveries applicable to their problems."

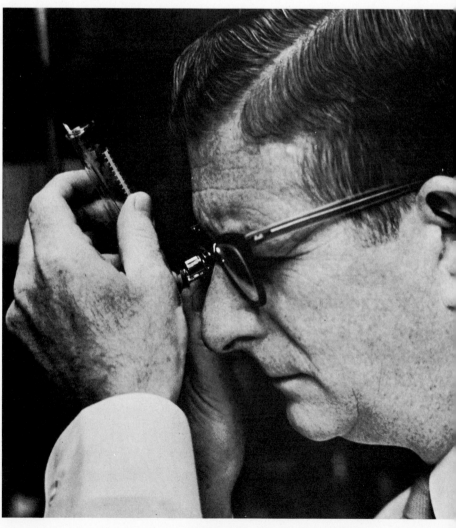

A ROSTER OF ATTRIBUTES

Robert Landel, 37, head of the polymer research section of the Jet Propulsion laboratory in Pasadena, California, stretches a rubber band as he discusses his current specialty—the uses of rubber as a binder in solid rocket fuels. The prime attributes of a good scientist, Landel feels, are "a simple determination to work hard, a good memory, an ability in mathematics and a talent for analysis and description." As for his own memory, Landel once had some doubts. Early in the course of his schooling he was anxious to take up the study of ornithology, but decided against it. "The thought of memorizing all those feathers," he recalls, "horrified me."

43

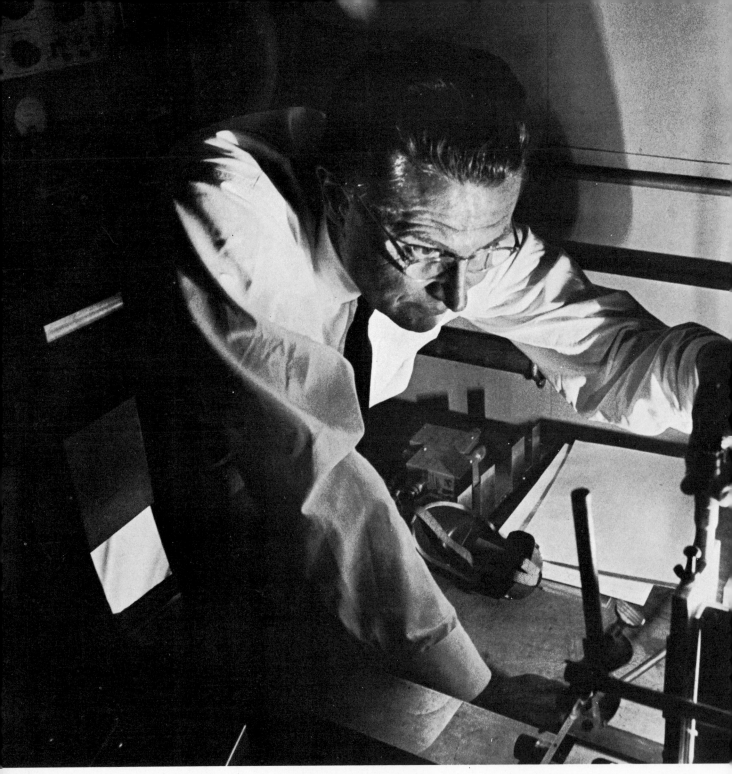

A PRODUCT OF IMPORTANCE

The glare of hot gases lights the face of Sanborn Brown, 50, as he observes a dense plasma reaction in his laboratory at the Massachusetts Institute of Technology, where he is an associate dean. The basic data he gathers may one day contribute to the use of controlled fusion. Brown does not rate theoretical physics over applied physics or vice versa. "Some people like to solve useful problems," he says, "while others get satisfaction in just understanding what's going on." Even more than research, Brown enjoys teaching. "My most important product is people. My satisfaction comes from the education I can give people"—and not necessarily just on the graduate level. "You can learn as much in the fourth grade as you do getting your Ph.D."

The Power and Promise of Extreme Hot and Cold

Nothing more clearly illustrates the vast range that physics has claimed as its own than the work of the two men shown on these pages. Sanborn Brown *(left)* is concerned with plasma physics, involving the so-called fourth state of matter—a mass of superexcited, electrically charged particles at extremely high temperatures (the sun and stars are composed of plasma). Stanford's William M. Fairbank *(below),* on the other hand, is devoted to the opposite end of the temperature spectrum— the field of cryogenics, which deals with cold in the neighborhood of absolute zero.

Though seemingly opposite to each other, the work of these two men is curiously intertwined. In Brown's specialty a crucial problem is the confinement of plasmas so hot that no container yet devised can hold them. Oddly, studies of cold may provide the answer. Fairbank is using powerful cryogenic magnets which may be able to contain plasmas within their fields without direct contact with them. "If so," says Fairbank, "we will have reached the ultimate in the absurdity of science, a 'bottle'—269° C. cold, to contain a process involving millions of degrees of heat."

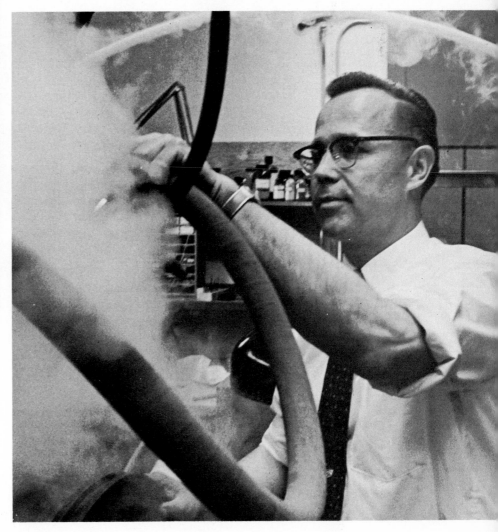

THE GOOD OF "GOING WRONG"
Surrounded by hoses and puffs of water vapor, William M. Fairbank, 46, of Stanford University in California, inspects the apparatus of an experiment involving matter at supercold temperatures. In addition to his research, Fairbank also teaches. He makes a particular point of looking for outstanding career students on the undergraduate level. His criteria: "A combination of curiosity and productive originality, coupled with self-confidence. Curiosity speaks for itself. Originality that isn't productive is useless. And self-confidence has to be enlightened." Added to this, Fairbank asserts, failure is also a part of training. "What [a student] needs is for everything to go wrong. Then he has to pick up the pieces and go on. That's when he learns."

A SINGLE PREOCCUPATION

Slight, energetic, possessed of a puckish sense of humor and a brilliant mind preoccupied with physics nearly 24 hours a day, Tsung Dao Lee, 36, discusses his favorite subject during a stroll at Columbia University in New York. Lee says that in his work a command of mathematics is vital, since "equations are the tools." And he is "at work" almost continually. "Research is a constant thing," he says. "You cannot count the hours—almost all the hours in the day." Married and the father of two children, Lee was born in Shanghai and came to the United States in 1946 on a Chinese government fellowship. Ten years later he was a full professor at Columbia, the youngest on campus at the time.

A QUESTION OF DARING

Chen Ning Yang *(left)* is the other member of the team which upset the law of parity concerning the behavior of subatomic particles. Now with the Institute for Advanced Study at Princeton, Yang asserts that for all of the momentum of science today, "the more we study nature, the more complex the picture gets." A Nobel Prize-winner at 34, Yang, now 40, believes that youth is an actual advantage in scientific work. "As you get older, you get less daring. . . . For every new thought you have, you immediately marshal a large number of counterarguments. You are afraid to proceed. When you are younger you pursue new ideas immediately. Have I lost my daring? I often ask myself that question."

From the Foreign-born, a Boon for U.S. Science

The pre-eminence of the United States in physics today is due in large measure to the contribution of foreign-born scientists who chose, often for political reasons, to come and work here. The most renowned, of course, was Albert Einstein, who fled Germany in the early days of Hitler. And there was the remarkable Italian, Enrico Fermi, famed as a Nobel Prize-winner who was a teacher as well. From Hungary came Edward Teller, and from Germany Hans Bethe. Without such men as these the United States could never have taken such an impressive lead in the field of nuclear physics.

Since World War II, America has continued to attract scientific talent. But now the influx from abroad consists mainly of students, mostly working toward their Ph.D.s. One out of every 10 graduate students in this country has come from other lands and intends to return at the end of his training.

Two of the three distinguished Chinese physicists on these pages, Tsung Dao Lee and Chen Ning Yang *(opposite)*, came to this country as graduate students and decided to remain. In 1957 they shared the Nobel Prize in physics when, by brilliant reasoning, they upset the sacrosanct law of conservation of parity. Essentially, this law held that when an atomic nucleus decays, the particles it emits would be just as likely to spin in one direction as the other. Lee and Yang suggested, instead, that each type of elementary particle given off during radioactive decay has a characteristic spin—a hypothesis validated in the laboratory by the brilliant woman physicist Dr. Chien-Shiung Wu *(below)*.

A BREAK WITH TRADITION

A renowned experimentalist in physics, Dr. Chien-Shiung Wu, 50, stands amidst some tubes of a particle accelerator at her Columbia University laboratory. Perhaps most famed for an experiment which confirmed the disproval of parity by Lee and Yang *(opposite)*, Mme. Wu has many other achievements to her credit, mainly in the fields of subatomic particles. Married to a physicist and mother of a teen-age son, she believes that the U.S. academic atmosphere is not conducive to a scientific career for women because it is considered "unladylike." But those who have broken with tradition "have been doing quite well," in Dr. Wu's opinion. "To have a husband as a scientist is a great help," she says. "Then you can sometimes talk physics."

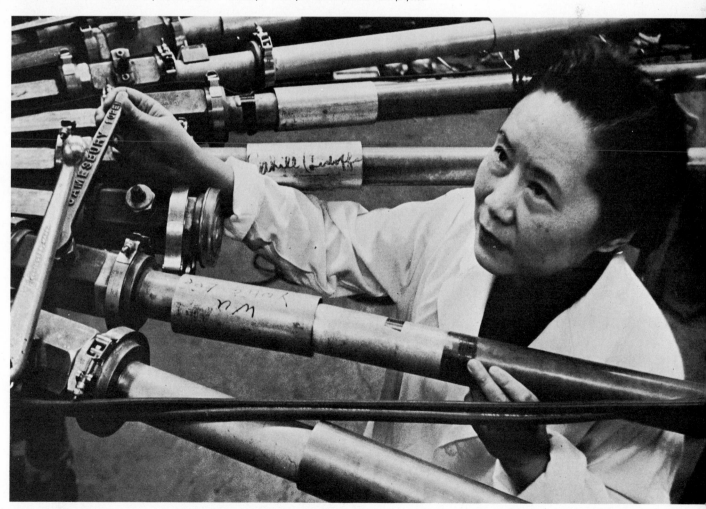

An Urge
to Educate the
Young

Scratch almost any scientist and you will find a teacher underneath. Many top men teach huge freshman classes, though most limit themselves to small seminars of graduate students. One teacher may have as many as a dozen Ph.D. candidates working toward their degrees under his direction.

Of all Ph.D. candidates, about 10 per cent—approximately 11,000—are in the fields of physics and chemistry. This percentage remains fairly constant, since it represents those students with sufficient interest and drive to find science attrac-

tive. But educators are constantly hoping to expand this number, and promising undergraduates are regularly sought after.

Despite the dearth of science students, the science curriculum grows apace. A big school like the University of Illinois has 30 physics research specialties alone, from superconductivity to magnetic resonance. Undergraduate colleges like Whitman (opposite) feature advanced physics courses. Western Reserve University in Cleveland offers research in positron annihilation, and the University of Alaska, fittingly, has a specialty in "aurora phenomena."

A CONCEPT OF LIGHT AND SHADOW
Dudley Herschbach energetically puts across a point to a student at the University of California. Only 30, Herschbach was appointed a full professor of chemistry at Harvard in 1963. His most noteworthy research contribution to date has been to study chemical reactions by observing collisions of gas molecules—a technique borrowed from physics. As a teacher, Herschbach assumes students know "printing has been invented." He feels that a "teacher is not someone to dispense material that is already in a book, but someone who can put light and shadow on it—a spiritual father, if you will."

FREE REIN FOR MAVERICKS
Walter Brattain poses a question to a class in advanced physics at Whitman College, Walla Walla, Washington (enrollment only 850). Brattain spends three weeks of each month at Bell Telephone Laboratories in New Jersey, where, as a research physicist, he helped develop the transistor, which won him a Nobel Prize. Once a month he travels some 5,000 miles round trip to spend a week teaching at Whitman, his alma mater. Brattain believes that small schools encourage independent thinking. They are, he thinks, places where "the mavericks can have free rein . . . and that is definitely good for all."

$A_c - A_\infty = -\frac{2}{\pi}\int_0^\infty \frac{B\omega - (B\omega)_c}{\omega^2 - \omega_c^2}\,d\omega$
A
B
W

3

The Wayward, Willful Ways of Gas

THE THREE familiar states of matter—solid, liquid and gas—can best be summed up in terms of human analogy. A solid is akin to a platoon of soldiers standing at stiff attention in closed ranks. A liquid is like an unruly mob, surging now this way, now that. A gas resembles a bunch of youngsters playing at random on a large lot, and occasionally bumping into one another; their behavior would be rather chaotic, and the word gas, in fact, stems from the Greek word *chaos*.

Seemingly, gases should be the most baffling of the forms of matter; they are the most tenuous, and more often than not intangible. To the layman, these will-o'-the-wisp substances are indeed an enigma, even though they appear everywhere in life—as the air we breathe, the smelly fuel of a kitchen stove, the Freon gas of an air conditioner, the filling of toy balloons, the air which inflates tires, the oxygen and acetylene of a welding torch, the anesthetic that brings relief on the operating table.

To the scientist, on the other hand, gases are paradoxically the form of matter he knows most about. For individual gas molecules are so widely spaced, compared to those of a liquid or solid, that one molecule acts more or less independently of another; their collective behavior is therefore easier to survey.

Although one state of matter can, at a certain temperature, pass over into another, each state has its own unique properties. The traits of a gas reflect the free and easy manner of its molecules.

To begin with, gases are springy. The slightest impact in the air sets unfettered molecules knocking against each other. This creates waves of sound; the mere scraping of a cricket's wings causes such a molecular commotion that it can be heard half a mile off. The same springiness shoots the cork out of a champagne bottle and drives the noisy pneumatic hammers that break up our pavements.

Gases also readily intermix and diffuse through each other. A bottle of perfume left open will soon scent a whole room, for as the perfume evaporates, its gas molecules diffuse and are wafted about by drafts until distributed throughout the air. The air itself is a homogeneous mixture of gases; whether it hovers over an arctic waste or the African veld, it contains very nearly the same proportions of nitrogen, oxygen and other gases.

Gases have no natural shape of their own and expand freely to fill any container. Neon lights follow the curves of script in an advertising sign because the gas inside accommodates itself to any shape of glass tubing. Further, the volume of a gas varies with its pressure and temperature. A balloon expands as it soars into "thinner" air where pressure is lower; it contracts as a cloud blocks the sun.

When they expand, gases cool, and when compressed they heat up. Anyone who has ever pumped up a tire by hand knows that the pump gets hot, and so does the tire. This same idiosyncrasy of gas has made possible

A HYDROGEN HOLOCAUST
The explosion of the German zeppelin *Hindenburg* at Lakehurst, New Jersey, on May 6, 1937 *(opposite)*, was caused by the fiery union of its 6.7 million cubic feet of hydrogen with oxygen of the air around it. The holocaust destroyed the ship and 35 lives in less than five minutes. Shunning the highly flammable hydrogen, modern lighter-than-air craft use unburnable helium.

the refrigerator: an electric pump compresses the refrigerant gas, which expands through a series of coils, cools the interior of the refrigerator as it expands, then re-enters the compressor for a new cycle.

Like liquids, gases flow. This fluidity allows natural gas to pour through "big inch" pipelines all over the country, enabling a New England housewife to burn gas in her stove that five days earlier was buried deep in the crust of Texas.

The properties of a gas are perhaps most dramatically demonstrated in the dazzling blast that thrusts a missile into outer space. But an even more spectacular show lies hidden in the microscopic world of gas molecules. In this subsurface realm a gas appears as a cloud of free molecules which career at tremendous speeds through a void, spinning, ricocheting and colliding almost without restraint. Molecules in the air beat against a windowpane at the rate of two million billion billion molecules per square inch per second. For their size, these molecules are relatively distant from one another, but because of the speed at which the average molecule moves—1,000 miles per hour—it collides with its fellows five billion times per second. These collisions, however, are "elastic." As in the crackups of small "dodge 'em" cars in an amusement park, the molecules bounce off each other without dissipating energy.

A square inch of fury

It is the ceaseless fury of molecular motion and collision that accounts for the characteristic behavior of a gas. The impact of two million billion billion molecules against a square inch of windowpane every second would shatter the glass if an equal number of molecular blows were not being rained against it, just as often, from the other side of the pane; such enormous force of gas pressure is what powers a steam engine or turbojet. The springiness of a gas, too, is a result of its disorderly molecular conduct; the more it is compressed, the more its molecules crowd together, the more they bump into the compressor's surface, thereby offering a springy resistance to it. A gas can diffuse, mix and fill a container of any shape, size or form because of the utter abandon with which its molecules gad about.

The molecular motion of a gas is measured in its temperature. Expanding a gas cools it because, in moving farther apart, its molecules must push others aside. This is tiring work even for ebullient gas molecules; it slows them down, and a lower temperature results. Conversely, compressing a gas warms it because, as the molecules are shoved closer together, the shove speeds them up, giving the gas a higher temperature.

Although more is now known about gases than either solids or liquids, gases were the last to be identified as a distinct state of matter. Until the 17th Century, with its proliferation of scientific techniques and tools,

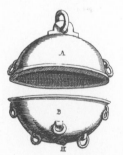

gases remained hard to capture and analyze. They could not, like solids, be broken, bent, powdered or piled high on the chemist's shelf; they could not, like liquids, be poured, soaked up, frozen or boiled. Man's knowledge of them was based essentially on speculation.

The Greeks were the first to recognize that air had substance. In the Fifth Century B.C., the philosopher Empedocles described the workings of a clepsydra, or water clock—a bulbous vessel with holes at either end, used to transfer liquids. When pushed into water with the upper end closed off, it would not fill up; when the upper opening was unblocked so that air could escape, water moved in. The air in the vessel, Empedocles concluded, had resisted the influx of the water.

Satisfied that air had substance, the Greeks conjectured that it also had weight, but were unable to confirm this experimentally. Then the all-knowing Aristotle, a century after Empedocles, decided that an empty space could not exist in nature. The convenient catch phrase "nature abhors a vacuum" sufficed for the next 2,000 years to explain the effects of weightiness of air in early siphons, bellows and pumps.

Yet no scholar who subscribed to the Aristotelian thesis could explain why nature's distaste for a vacuum stopped at 33 feet: as any plumber knew, water would not rise any higher than this in an evacuated pipe. Even the great Galileo, whose experiments heralded the scientific renaissance of 17th Century Europe, was puzzled. Then, without realizing it, he provided the answer in an ingeniously simple experiment which established that air has weight. On his scales he balanced a sealed vessel, containing nothing but air at normal atmospheric pressure, against a heap of sand. Then he pumped more air into the vessel, resealed it, put it back on the scales and found that it now outweighed the sand. Galileo reasoned that the added weight of the vessel could be due only to the increased amount of air inside.

Wisdom in a well

An Italian mathematician, Evangelista Torricelli, took Galileo's finding the necessary step further. The 35-year-old Torricelli had come to Florence to engage in scientific research with the aged master, and had found Galileo confined to his house by the Inquisition. Striking out on experiments of his own, he soon perceived what Galileo had not: that when a pipe was sunk into a well and evacuated, it was the surrounding air weighing down on the well water that pushed water up into the pipe. Torricelli guessed that the atmosphere simply was not heavy enough to push water higher than 33 feet.

To prove his point, he devised a scaled-down experiment; instead of water he used mercury, which is 13.6 times as dense. He sealed a 48-inch glass tube at one end and filled it to the brim with mercury. Stopping

WEIGHING THE ATMOSPHERE IN ITALY

TORRICELLI'S BAROMETER

"We live submerged at the bottom of an ocean of air," said the Italian scientist Evangelista Torricelli (1608-1647) above, who proved it by inventing an instrument that measured the weight of this airy "ocean"—the barometer. First he poured mercury into a glass tube through the open end *(below left)*. Then he inverted the tube and placed it in a crucible of mercury *(below right)*. The mercury ran down to level *a*. It did not run out of the tube because the weight of air pressed down on the mercury in the crucible with such strength that it supported the column in the tube.

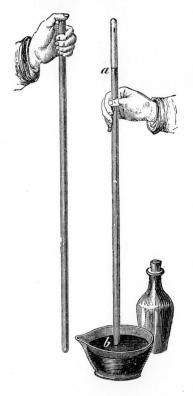

the open end with his finger, he then inverted the tube into a bowl also filled with mercury. When he removed his finger, the mercury in the tube dropped some 18 inches, leaving that much a vacuum. The liquid now stood at a height of 30 inches. This proved that the pressure of the air on the surface of the bowl equaled the pressure of the 30 inches of mercury in the tube. The device which Torricelli constructed for this historic experiment of 1643 was, incidentally, the world's first barometer. Even today the "barometric pressure" of the air is given in weather reports in Torricellian terms, as inches or millimeters "of mercury."

News of Torricelli's experiment reached the young French mathematician and philosopher Blaise Pascal, who determined to repeat it on a grand scale. Pascal managed to obtain a pair of 46-foot-long glass tubes; he filled one of them with water, the other with red wine, and found that the weight of air under normal conditions could support 33 feet of water (slightly more of wine) just as it upheld 30 inches of mercury. More importantly, from Torricelli's observation that the pressure exerted by the air at a given place must be due to the weight of air above it, Pascal concluded that differences in altitude must affect air pressure.

Experimenting along this line, he used a barometer to compare the air pressure at street level and atop a church steeple. When the results proved inconclusive, Pascal was undeterred. He had his brother-in-law, Florin Perier, place a barometer at the base of Mont Puy de Dôme in central France and carry another one to the peak, 3,200 feet up. The mercury turned out to stand three inches lower at the mountain's top, a fact which, Perier reported back to his learned relative, "ravished us with admiration and astonishment." This experiment, like Torricelli's, had a significant side result. In showing that the earth's atmospheric pressure decreases at higher altitudes, Pascal demonstrated that a barometer, which measures changing pressures, can also be used as an altimeter to measure altitudes above sea level.

Marvels of a burgomaster

With their use of the scale and barometer to investigate the air, Galileo, Torricelli and Pascal started the scientific study of gases. Another advance was achieved by the construction of the first vacuum pump powerful enough to empty the air out of virtually any container. This device was built by a German engineer and burgomaster, Otto von Guericke, and the wonders he performed with it gave him the status of a miracle worker: in his vacuums a burning candle was snuffed out as the air was exhausted, grapes were preserved, sounds failed to travel, and animals quickly died.

In time Von Guericke's local fame spread: one day in 1654 when he combined showmanship and science in his most celebrated experiment,

MAKING AIR SPLIT CONCRETE
Powered by compressed air, a pneumatic hammer can pound away at pavement with a machine-gun speed of more than 2,000 blows a minute. Touching the finger lever opens the air inlet to fill the piston chamber behind the piston. This knocks the piston against the chipping tool, which then strikes a blow against the concrete. Meanwhile, the return air valve changes its position so that air can shoot through the return air passage to force the piston back to its original position.

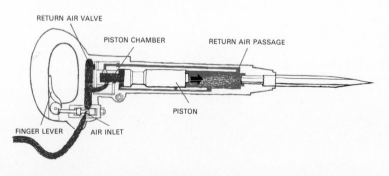

RETURN AIR VALVE

PISTON CHAMBER

RETURN AIR PASSAGE

PISTON

FINGER LEVER   AIR INLET

the emperor himself was in attendance. From a local smith Von Guericke had obtained two hollow bronze hemispheres, each about 20 inches in diameter. He fitted them together at the rims and pumped out the air. A team of horses was then hitched to each hemisphere. As the awestruck emperor and throng watched, the horses exerted all their might in their effort to pull the hemispheres apart. Yet they were held together, as Von Guericke assured the assemblage, solely by the pressure of the outside air.

At this mid-point in the 17th Century word began to circulate about the work of Johann Baptista van Helmont, a Belgian chemist and physician, who had died in 1644 after 13 years of investigation by the Inquisition, imprisonment and house arrest. Author of the word gas, Van Helmont was also the first man to recognize that there are different kinds of gases, and that the "substance" of air is one of them. In a memorable experiment, he applied steady heat to 62 pounds of charcoal in a closed vessel and found the vessel's weight unchanged even though the charcoal was reduced to one pound of ash; he concluded that the other 61 pounds had turned into "wild spirit" which could not escape. Casting about for an apt descriptive, Van Helmont drew upon the Greek word *chaos:* "I call this spirit, hitherto unknown, by the new name of gas, which can neither be retained in vessels nor reduced to a visible form...."

The fate of a floating candle

Van Helmont shared many of the popular credulities of his time. He was convinced, for example, that mice could be produced in three weeks by "spontaneous generation" from wheat in a glass stopped with dirty linen. He believed that the herb basil, if crushed in a cavity between two bricks, would spawn scorpions. Along with such fancies, however, he managed to acquire a good deal of information about gases. In one experiment he floated a burning candle on water and covered it with an inverted glass cup. Noting that the flame went out and the water level within the cup rose, he wrote: "There is in air something that is less than a body, which fills up the vacuities in the air and is wholly annihilated by fire." Although this gas—oxygen—was not identified for another century and a half, Van Helmont did distinguish 14 other gases. He found them in such disparate places as the bubbling water of spas and the large intestine of man. Because he lacked adequate equipment for analysis, Van Helmont's list of gases contained duplications, but it included a number of gases recognized today, among them carbon monoxide, carbon dioxide, sulphur dioxide and nitric oxide.

Van Helmont's notes on gases were read in England by Robert Boyle, who, as we have seen in earlier pages, was the formulator of the modern concept of the elements. Intrigued by the Belgian's work, as well as by

EXPANSIVE AND COLD, RESTRICTED AND HOT

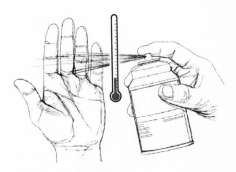

A CHILLING SPRAY
In an aerosol can *(above)*, a liquid and a compressed gas are released as a fine spray. As indicated by the thermometer, the spray is cold because a compressed gas loses heat when it expands. Spray insecticide may freeze plant leaves if the nozzle is held too close.

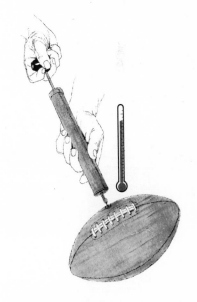

A HOT COMPRESSION
A piston pump *(above)* compresses air into a football. The thermometer indicates that the air in the pump is hotter than room temperature because a gas gains heat when its molecules are pushed closer together. A pump frequently gets too hot to touch.

HARNESSING THE AIR TO TAP A WELL

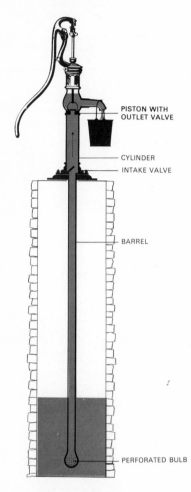

PISTON WITH OUTLET VALVE

CYLINDER

INTAKE VALVE

BARREL

PERFORATED BULB

A GIANT MEDICINE DROPPER

The hand-operated pump *(above)* is still used for drawing water in parts of rural America. It works like an enormous medicine dropper, though with more complex machinery. The weight of the atmosphere on underground water pushes it up the barrel in which a pumping action has created a partial vacuum— like the one made by squeezing and releasing the rubber of a dropper. The four steps below show how water is brought to the bucket.

reports of Von Guericke's air pump and vacuum experiments and Pascal's mountain test of atmospheric pressure, Boyle set to work in his laboratory, the best-equipped of his time, and performed an experiment which, barring all his other achievements, would have accorded him a place in scientific annals.

Boyle marked each leg of a J-shaped tube with a scale and sealed off the shorter leg. He then poured mercury into the longer leg, trapping air in the other until the mercury in both parts of the tube was at the same level; the trapped air, Boyle reasoned, was now exerting a pressure exactly equal to the air pressure outside the tube. Then he continued to pour mercury into the open end of the tube until the volume of trapped air was halved. To achieve this required an added 30 inches of mercury, and Boyle knew from Torricelli's experiment that 30 inches of mercury was equivalent to the weight, or pressure, of the atmosphere. Thus he had doubled the pressure in order to halve the volume of trapped air, proving that pressure and volume vary inversely. This is what is now known as Boyle's law. Boyle probably recognized that his law held true only at constant temperature, but the precise mode of temperature variation was not established until after his time. Eventually Boyle's law was further qualified as strictly applicable only to an "ideal" gas—one in which there are *no* forces acting between molecules; in real gases small intermolecular forces—called Van der Waals forces for the Dutchman who postulated their existence—cause slight deviations from Boyle's pressure-volume relationship.

An early expert on smog

Boyle's experiments had concentrated on the physical nature of gases. To ascertain their chemical properties, better means had to be found for collecting and analyzing them. It was a Londoner of the next century, Henry Cavendish, who broke first ground in this field. Cavendish was probably the first smog expert of history, gathering air samples from every quarter of the city; he may also, with some justification, be described as the first "space scientist," having collected samples of the upper air by means of a balloon. He is best remembered, however, for an experiment which he performed with the new "dephlogisticated air" discovered by his fellow countryman Joseph Priestley in 1774 (actually, a Swedish apothecary, Carl Wilhelm Scheele, had already discovered it, as "fire air," several years earlier). As noted in Chapter 2, the French scientific genius Antoine Lavoisier was to identify this substance and name it oxygen; currently, however, it was being acclaimed for the "splendor" and "sparkle" with which it made things burn. Cavendish burned carefully measured amounts of the new "air" together with hydrogen and found that the two gases were completely converted into their own weight

PISTON WITH OUTLET VALVE

INTAKE VALVE

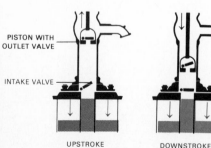

UPSTROKE   DOWNSTROKE

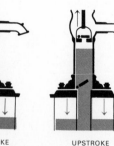

UPSTROKE

DOWNSTROKE

HOW A SUCTION PUMP WORKS

The first upstroke *(far left)* of the piston increases the volume of the cylinder. This creates a partial vacuum and the air pressure *(arrows)* pressing on the water in the well pushes it up into the pump pipe. After a downstroke, another upstroke brings the water still higher into the pump cylinder itself. The last downstroke pushes the water up toward the faucet and finally out into the bucket.

of water. This was the first quantitative proof that water was a compound of hydrogen and oxygen.

Across the Channel, Lavoisier repeated the experiment in several ways with his superior scales. He not only burned oxygen and hydrogen to produce water; he also reversed the process and decomposed water into the two gases. He also showed that water could be vaporized into steam, then recondensed with no change in weight. Lavoisier took the results of these experiments to support his cardinal principle, that in chemical reactions, matter—whether solid, liquid or gaseous—is neither created nor destroyed. This theory he supplemented by other exhaustive studies of the combustion of various substances—phosphorus, charcoal, olive oil, wax—and by research on fermentation and putrefaction.

The birth of a bestseller

Lavoisier's broad talents extended well beyond experimentation. He consolidated much fragmented information about gases; he also decided to "improve the chemical language" of his day. Inevitably, this led him to write his own extensive tome on chemistry, because, he said, he could not separate "the nomenclature of a science from the science itself." The resulting *Traité Elémentaire de Chimie (Elements of Chemistry)*, with a beautifully illustrated section on the instruments of the chemist's laboratory, proved an enormous success, gaining added circulation beyond his own land in English, Dutch, Spanish, Italian and Mexican editions.

Even as earlier luminaries of science had suffered at the hands of a religious inquisition, so Lavoisier was doomed by a secular tribunal. As a young man he had bought a third interest in a share in the Farmers-General, a financial corporation with a royal license to collect taxes from the populace; the income paid the bills for his experiments. But with the French Revolution, all the directors of the hated Farmers-General were charged with graft and sentenced to the guillotine. An appeal for clemency for Lavoisier was turned down thus: "The Republic has no need of savants." He was executed in 1794.

The political ferment of the times had its counterpart in a mounting intellectual tempest. As activity heightened along every scientific front, Europe's chemists were rent by a historic controversy. In England, John Dalton, in the course of devising the system of atomic weights described in the preceding chapter, advanced the monumental concept that every element is composed of identical atoms of the same weight and that these combine in various ways to form what he described as "compound atoms" (now called molecules). This idea was consistent with empirical observations that when one element combines in two different ways with a fixed weight of another element, the two weights of the first element are in the ratio of whole numbers. But Dalton's theory did not explain

TOOLS AND TOYS THAT WORK BY AIR

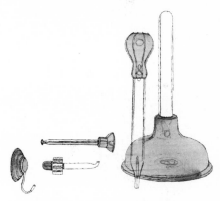

THE SCIENCE BEHIND SUCTION

A suction cup, a medicine dropper, a toy dart, a turkey baster and a plunger *(above)* work by air pressure. All are basically variations on the simple suction cup, which works by the three steps shown below. (1) When the cup is not pressed to a surface, air pressure *(heavy arrows)* is equal on all sides. (2) Squeezing it flat against a wall forces out much of the air *(light arrows)*. (3) The elastic cup bounces back to its original shape, causing a partial vacuum *(lower air pressure)* inside of it. The higher pressure outside *(heavy arrows)* holds the cup against the wall.

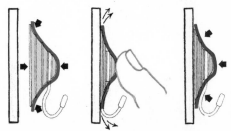

EQUAL PRESSURE   DECREASING PRESSURE   PARTIAL VACUUM

the remarkable finding by a French chemist, Joseph Gay-Lussac, that
one volume of oxygen and one volume of nitrogen produced not *one* volume of nitric oxide but *two*. Dalton insisted that gases consisted of single atoms in close contact with each other, and that therefore only *one* volume of nitric oxide could result from one volume of nitrogen and one volume of oxygen. He even accused Gay-Lussac of careless measurement.

A late-blooming hypothesis

In 1811, amid all the acrimony, an Italian professor of physics, Amedeo Avogadro, put forth a hypothesis which later determined the entire course of scientific thinking on gases and their composition. Avogadro made two bold guesses: that gaseous elements—quite unlike solids or liquids—exist in diatomic molecules, that is, molecules of two atoms each; and that equal volumes of gases at the same temperature and pressure contain the same number of molecules. Thus Gay-Lussac's single volumes of oxygen and nitrogen contained twice as many atoms as Dalton supposed, and *could* produce two volumes of nitric oxide. In the heat of the dispute, Avogadro's hypothesis was overlooked, partly because he failed to make clear his concept of the molecule, using instead the catch-all word "particle." It was not until almost 50 years later that another Italian, the chemist Stanislao Cannizzaro, dusted off Avogadro's hypothesis and used it to determine the atomic weights of gases more precisely. (Avogadro was later honored by having a physical constant named for him. Avogadro's number—which he himself never heard of—is the number of gas molecules contained in one "mole": the amount which occupies 22.4 liters at standard conditions of temperature and pressure. Numerically, it is 6.02×10^{23}, or 600,000 billion billion molecules.)

While the chemists were still bickering over the question of how gases combine, a physicist named Michael Faraday—son of an English blacksmith—was pursuing a wholly new line of investigation with enormous practical implications for the future. In 1823 Faraday decided to find out what happened when a gas was compressed and chilled. Using a bent glass tube, he placed the crystals of a chlorine compound in the shorter leg, sealed the tube, then immersed the longer leg in a freezing mixture. Heating the crystals caused chlorine gas to be released and pressure to build up. As the gas moved over into the cold area of the tube, it began to condense.

This was the first of many experiments in which Faraday liquefied a gas. He used the same technique on hydrogen sulphide (which gives rotten eggs their notorious smell), sulphur dioxide, ammonia and other gases. But he could not succeed with oxygen or nitrogen or hydrogen; these, in fact, came to be called "permanent gases" because of their reluctance to go into a liquid state. Eventually it was realized that every

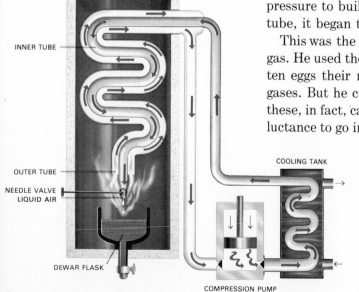

INNER TUBE

OUTER TUBE

NEEDLE VALVE
LIQUID AIR

DEWAR FLASK

COOLING TANK

COMPRESSION PUMP

LIQUEFYING THE ATMOSPHERE

To liquefy air, it must first be compressed by a
pump and run through a cooling tank. The
resulting cold compressed air then escapes
through the inner tube of a double-walled coil.
Passing through a needle valve, it expands so
quickly that its temperature drops sharply.
The air then travels up the outer tube of the
coil and back to the compressor, where the
cycle resumes. It continues until the air cools to
−317.2° F., when it liquefies and drops into
a Dewar flask where it can be stored.

gas has a "critical temperature" above which it cannot be liquefied. For the permanent kind these temperatures are incredibly low.

Such a temperature was attained for oxygen in 1877 by two men working independently: Louis Paul Cailletet, an ironmaster in Châtillon-sur-Seine, France, and Raoul Pictet, a professor of physics in Geneva. The critical temperature of oxygen proved to be a subarctic −182°F. Within 30 years every known gas had been liquefied; the last to succumb was helium in 1908, at the hands of H. Kamerlingh Onnes, a Dutch physicist. The critical point at which helium became a liquid was −452°F.—only 7.7°F. above "absolute zero," the temperature at which zigzagging molecules would come to a quivering standstill.

Helium and gases related to it were not only difficult to liquefy: they were also hard to find. Called "inert" or "noble" gases because they snubbed other elements, they were tracked down in one of the great sagas of chemical detection. Their trail had been picked up as early as 1785 when Henry Cavendish, in one experiment with air, noticed a small bubble of gas "not more than 1/120th part of the whole" which would not partake in the chemical reaction. The importance of this observation was not realized for more than a century. In 1894 two Englishmen, J.W.S. Rayleigh and William Ramsay, observed this same mysterious gas in the air and analyzed it with a spectroscope, a device which identifies gases by the characteristic color lines they show when an electric current passes through them. This gas, which seemed to have no chemical properties at all, revealed red and green lines never before observed. Rayleigh and Ramsay named it argon, "the lazy one."

An accumulation of clues

Earlier, during an 1868 eclipse of the sun, a French astronomer, Pierre Jules César Janssen, had spotted a brilliant yellow line in the sun's spectrum. It was soon attributed to an unknown element, which was named after *helios*, the Greek word for the sun. Thirteen years later an Italian physicist, Luigi Palmieri, detected the same line in the effluvia of the crater of Vesuvius; an American chemist, William Hillebrand, subsequently isolated an inert gas with the same spectrum from a black uranium mineral. From all this accumulating data and from his own tests Ramsay identified helium. Not long thereafter the rest of the inert gases were found; Ramsay and his assistant, M. W. Travers, identified krypton, neon and xenon in 1898 by liquefying air and examining the residue left when the oxygen and nitrogen were evaporated. The last inert gas, radon, was discovered in 1900 by a German professor, Ernst Dorn, among the radioactive decay products of radium.

The best method of separating the air's mixed content of gases has proved to be the liquefaction of the air itself; this has grown into a

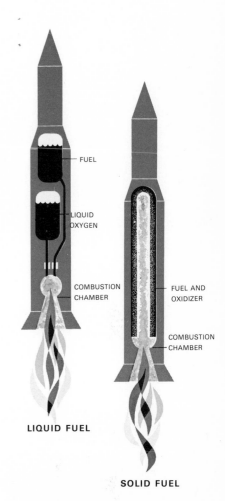

FUEL

LIQUID OXYGEN

COMBUSTION CHAMBER

LIQUID FUEL

FUEL AND OXIDIZER

COMBUSTION CHAMBER

SOLID FUEL

GAS PROPULSION INTO SPACE
A liquid fuel rocket *(above left)* carries a tank of fuel and a tank of liquid oxidizer. These unite in the combustion chamber, and the heat produced so expands the resulting gases that they "explode" out through the chamber to the tail pipe. In a solid fuel rocket *(above right)*, fuel and oxidizer are blended into a solid with a hollow shaft down its middle. A spark makes it burn from inside out. The force of the gases shooting from the tail hurls the rocket upward.

billion-dollar-a-year industry. By volume the air contains 78.09 per cent nitrogen; 20.95 per cent oxygen; 0.93 per cent argon; 0.02 to 0.04 per cent carbon dioxide; 0.0018 per cent neon; and traces of hydrogen, helium, krypton and xenon. As the liquid air is evaporated, each gas is drawn off at its own boiling point. Once isolated, these gases are invaluable. Helium is used in producing new high-strength, corrosion-resistant metals like zirconium; argon in welding; krypton in long-lasting light bulbs; xenon is an experimental anesthetic which brings near-natural sleep.

The technology of liquefied gases has grown phenomenally since World War II, when liquid oxygen was used in the engines of the German V-2 rockets showered on London. Our own space missiles today employ it as an oxidizer, and our astronauts breathe its vapor. An even more powerful space fuel combines liquid hydrogen and liquid fluorine: rocket engines using this mix are in development. Liquid oxygen, produced for less than five dollars a ton, speeds the operation of steel-making furnaces. Liquid nitrogen refrigerates food trucks, flash-freezes fruits and vegetables, and preserves whole blood and human body tissues for indefinite periods. Research at the supercold temperatures needed to liquefy these gases has opened up the new frontier of science called cryogenics, some of whose wonders are shown in the ensuing picture essay.

Such have been the tangible benefits to man of matter in its most tenuous form, once thought too elusive even to be examined.

The Eccentric Domain of the Supercold

The bite of frost, the knife-edge of a winter wind—these are what we usually associate with coldness. But rarely are frost and wind as cold as the "dry ice" in the ice cream wagon opposite. And even dry ice—the coldest thing (−109.3°F.) most people ever run into—is torrid in comparison with the supercold fluids achieved by cryogenics (from the Greek *kryos*, meaning icy cold, and the suffix *gen*, meaning producing). This new science studies the behavior of matter at fantastically low temperatures; it considers anything above −200°F. too hot to handle. It has managed to get down to within a millionth of a degree of "absolute zero," which is −459.7°F., the coldest possible temperature in the universe and the point at which atoms no longer move. As shown on the next pages, the commonplace acts in strange ways in cryogenics laboratories: electric currents flow in "perpetual" motion, and liquid defies gravity by creeping up and out of a bottle.

COOL POPS FROM BURNING ICE

The popsicle purchasers opposite can be sure of getting their money's worth unmelted because the wagon's contents are kept far below freezing by dry ice (frozen carbon dioxide), whose deep cold draws heat from the skin so rapidly that it paradoxically "burns" the fingers when touched. The same coldness causes the water vapor in the air to condense into the white mist.

Freakish Fluids That Defy Convention

If the thermometer should ever drop to −317.9°F., the old metaphor of the atmosphere as an "ocean of air" would become a reality: at that point air turns into a pale blue, inordinately cold liquid. Engulfed in such a sea, animal life would end. But in less overwhelming quantities liquid air is the wellspring of cryogenics.

The three main constituents of air are nitrogen (78.09 per cent), oxygen (20.95 per cent) and argon (0.93 per cent). When liquefied *(right)*, these elements have many extraordinary and useful properties *(opposite)*. Liquid argon, chemically inert, boils at −302.6°F., and is used in electronics to grow the tiny crystals of transistor radios. Liquid oxygen, chemically very active, boils at −297.4°F., and is in such demand for converting pig iron into steel and sending rockets into space that it is commercially produced at an estimated rate of one ton per second. Liquid nitrogen, chemically rather inactive, boiling at −320.5°F., is inexplosive, nontoxic and the best refrigerant for foods and living organs. It has already been employed to freeze blood for indefinite storage, and to preserve a chicken heart so that when thawed it resumed a healthy beat. Some "cryobiologists" believe that it may one day be used to keep an entire living organism in cold-storage hibernation for years.

BOILING AT ROOM TEMPERATURE
These three vacuum-insulated Dewar flasks (the chemist's equivalent of a Thermos bottle) contain, from bottom to top respectively, liquid argon, oxygen and nitrogen. The low boiling points of these liquids cause them to evaporate into their natural gaseous state when exposed to the normal heat of the laboratory; water vapor in the air is frozen into icy cloud formations.

UNDER EXTREME COLD, AN ODD REACTION IN FLOWERS AND METALS

When dunked into liquid nitrogen (first two pictures), a carnation is frozen so brittle that it cracks into splinters and fragments in the hand.

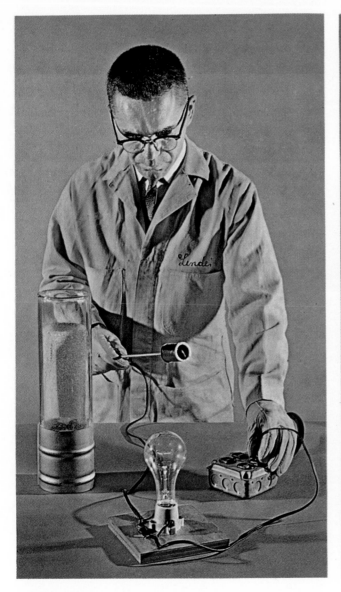

A FEEBLE GLOW
In the absence of cryogenic temperatures, the demonstrator above inserts a plug into a socket. This completes the electrical circuit through a coil of wire on a rod and the bulb. The long wire slows down electricity; the bulb barely glows.

A FURIOUS FLASH
The circuit above is the same as at left, but with the wire coil immersed in very cold liquid nitrogen. At its vastly lowered temperature, the coil loses all resistance to electricity and the bulb incandesces with a dazzling light.

From the Coolest Gases, the Hottest Rockets

First manufactured in 1932, liquid oxygen won world notoriety when used in the Nazi V-2s which rained destruction on London in 1944. These missiles worked much like today's. In the V-2, alcohol was burned with oxygen to form a hot vapor under pressure; the vapor then squeezed through a tail-pipe nozzle as a fiery jet that hurled the rocket into space. Because in its natural gaseous state oxygen takes up too much room for a rocket to carry it, the Germans used liquid oxygen, commercially called LOX, which occupies a mere fraction of the space of oxygen gas.

Today's rockets use fuels other than alcohol—kerosene in the case of the giants on these pages—but most of them continue to rely on liquid oxygen as their oxidizer. Many future rockets will use as fuel the extremely cold liquid hydrogen (boiling point −422.9°F.). This fluid is the ideal chemical fuel since it burns easily and, with the lowest atomic weight, produces the fastest-moving exhaust. When oxidized by LOX, the thrust is 40 per cent greater than that of a heavy kerosene-LOX jet. And although this light exhaust is no more than old-fashioned steam, it may well help propel the first manned expedition to another planet.

AN ASTRONAUT ON ICE AND FIRE
Trailing chunks of ice, an Atlas rocket *(right)* carrying astronaut Walter Schirra takes off. The frost forms as humidity in the air freezes on contact with the tanks of liquid oxygen. Because LOX is highly volatile, it is not loaded into the rocket until minutes before take-off.

LOX FOR A MOON PROBE
Surrounded by billows of chilled air, a Juno II rocket is shown below receiving a supply of LOX at Cape Canaveral (it needs 36 tons for the take-off). Juno's job was to propel the Pioneer IV space vehicle on a trip in 1959 to study the belts of radiation between earth and moon.

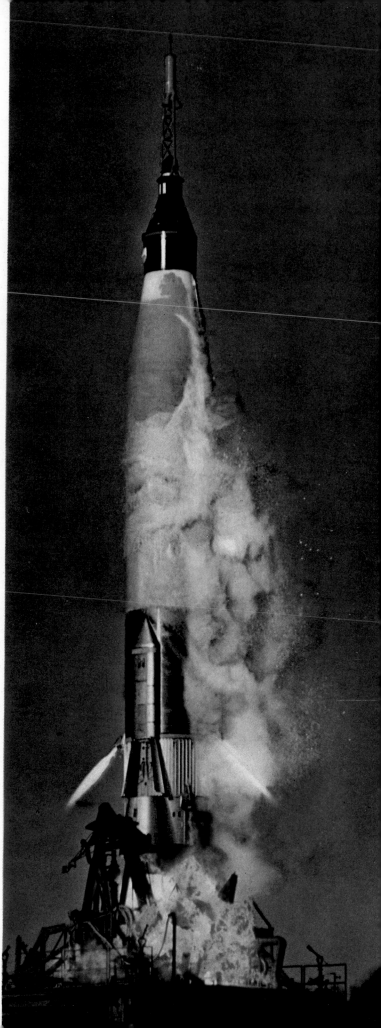

DESCENT INTO THE DEPTHS
In the photograph at left, a cryotron circuit like the one below is about to be lowered into a refrigerator of liquid helium to test the efficiency and durability of its metal conductors at very low temperatures. The refrigerator can maintain the temperature of −452° F. indefinitely.

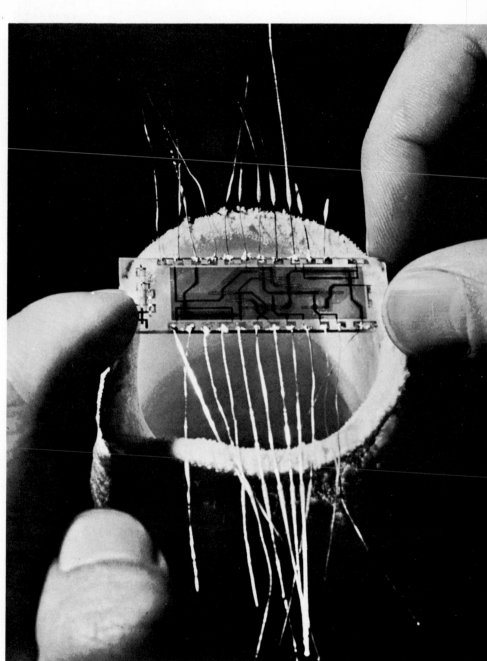

The Frigid Heart of Modern Computers

In the bleak abyss near "absolute zero," many metals suddenly lose *all* resistance to electricity. A current applied to such a circuit grows gradually stronger because there is nothing to stop it. If the voltage is removed, the current continues to flow through the circuit ceaselessly and at constant strength—the old fantasy of a perpetual-motion machine come true. It takes very little power to start such a current— and none at all to keep it going. As a result tiny superconducting circuits like the one opposite are revolutionizing those complex modern "thinking machines," electronic computers. When cooled to the −452°F. of liquid helium *(above and right)*, cryogenic computer circuits need so little power that it is possible to construct computers not only miniature in size but also fast as lightning in their performance.

THIN FILMS AND FAST ACTION
The circuit above is made into a superconductor by the almost rock-bottom temperature of the liquid helium below it. Although wires are attached, there are none inside the circuit; instead, it carries its currents on a grid of metallic films 20 millionths of an inch thick. Currents flowing in the vertical films of this grid create magnetic fields which switch off the currents in the horizontal films. This switching occurs so fast that it has never been accurately measured, but it is believed to take about 25 billionths of a second. Such incredible speeds are becoming more essential to computers as man gives them increasingly complex problems.

A COMPUTER'S BRAIN CELLS
Used in the fastest computers, a cryogenic "memory plane" is not much bigger than the ordinary straight pins placed alongside it in the highly enlarged photograph opposite. This unit has a network of 135 tiny rectangular cryotrons plated on its glass surface; these function as "brain cells" in a computer's memory. A plane this size can "remember" 40 pieces of information.

TAPPING A VERY COLD KEG
A flask of liquid helium is drawn from a cryostat *(above)*, a machine for liquefying gases. First the gas is compressed and cooled with another liquid gas. It is allowed to expand, which cools it further; then it is compressed, cooled and allowed to expand again. The process is repeated until the gas finally turns to a liquid.

The Outlandish Antics of Liquid Helium

Though named for the hottest spot in the solar system (*helios* is Greek for sun), helium gas can be turned into the coldest of fluids. It liquefies only at the fantastically low temperature of −452°F. When lowered four more degrees, it deviates so radically from its usual behavior that scientists rename it helium II. Among its many weird tricks, it makes metal magnets float in air *(opposite)* and casts a cold eye on gravity, flowing as if nothing at all were resisting its motion—as in the spouting fountain *(right)* and the creeping film *(opposite)*.

Scientists study its offbeat conduct to help them understand the more humdrum liquids in the same way that psychologists study aberrant humans to help them understand the average man. As of now, helium II is still held captive in the laboratory. Its slightly warmer cousin, helium I, is making its way in the world in such useful jobs as keeping rocket engines cool during the countdown process.

A FRANTIC FOUNTAIN
A weak light gives enough heat *(above)* to convert some of the helium II atoms in the thin tube into normal liquid helium. But bent on replacing the lost atoms, the helium II in the flask rushes up through a filter into the tube with such force that it shoots the liquid into the air.

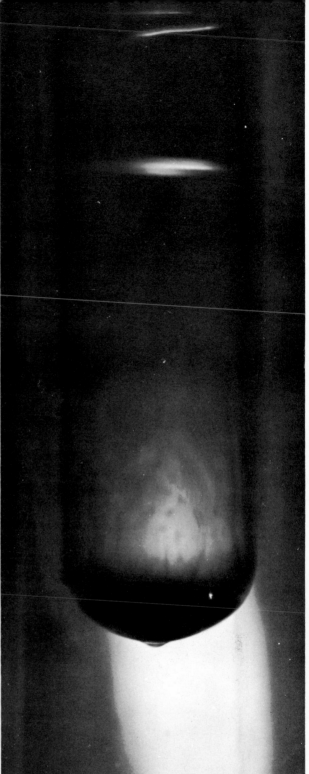

A CREEPING FILM
A beakerful of helium II *(above)*, when lifted from a pool of the same liquid, disports itself like no other substance known. It empties out of its container by creeping in a thin invisible film up the beaker's walls, over the edge, and down the outside to drop off at the bottom.

A HOVERING MAGNET
In a bath of liquid helium, a lead dish becomes a superconductor. When a small bar magnet is placed near it, the bar induces a current in the lead. Meeting no resistance, the current turns the lead into a powerful electromagnet that keeps the bar hovering above as shown at left.

69

Midgets
with the Muscle
of Giants

The huge electromagnets vital to modern research need millions of watts of power and thousands of gallons of water to cool them. Such requirements made ever-larger magnets impractical. Then came the discovery of small cryogenic superconductors which, when brought near the temperature of liquid helium, turn into powerhouses of magnetism. Their cores may be no larger than a fist *(right)*, but they pack the punch of old-style magnets that require roomfuls of machines in order to operate. Portable, needing no power at all to keep going, these midget magnets may be doing jobs that conventional magnets could never handle—removing metal particles from the body when surgery is impossible; forming a magnetic shield to protect astronauts from outer-space radiation.

STRENGTH FROM A COLD BATH
About to be immersed in liquid helium by Bell Laboratory physicists, the small cylinder of niobium-tin alloy above will become a formidable magnet with a strength of 24,000 gauss. (A toy horseshoe magnet is a few hundred gauss.) Niobium-tin, the best metal yet found for superconducting magnets, becomes instantly bereft of its potency when pulled from its icy bath.

PAPER CLIPS UNDER HYPNOSIS
A single magnet inside a Dewar flask of liquid helium at the Avco-Everett Laboratories in Everett, Massachusetts *(left)*, shows its power over 221 metal paper clips, each hanging freely from a tack. With the unblinking response of soldiers on a drill field, the clips marshal themselves in a formation which enables us to "see" the lines of force emanating from the magnet's poles.

MAN VERSUS MAGNET
The same magnet shown at left puts on another performance in the picture opposite. Its pull on the three-and-a-half-pound monkey wrench is so great that the wrench is kept from clanking against it only by the force which a grimacing technician exerts on the cord tied to the handle. Such magnets perform feats like this without needing the help of a single watt of electricity.

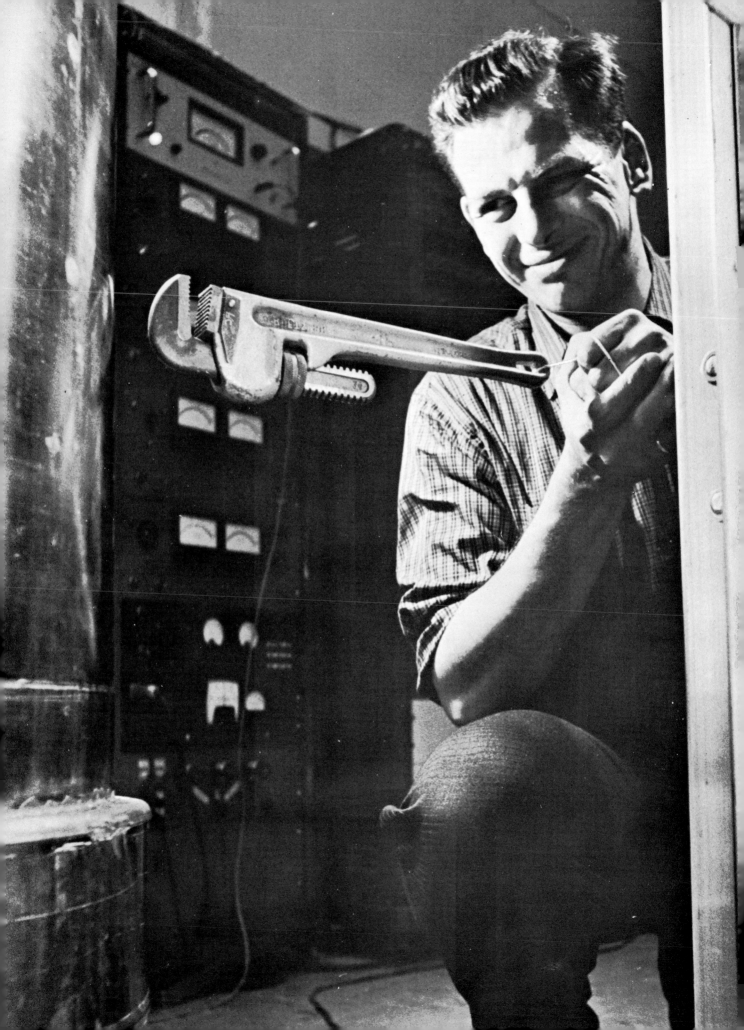

4

The Restless Surge of the Liquid State

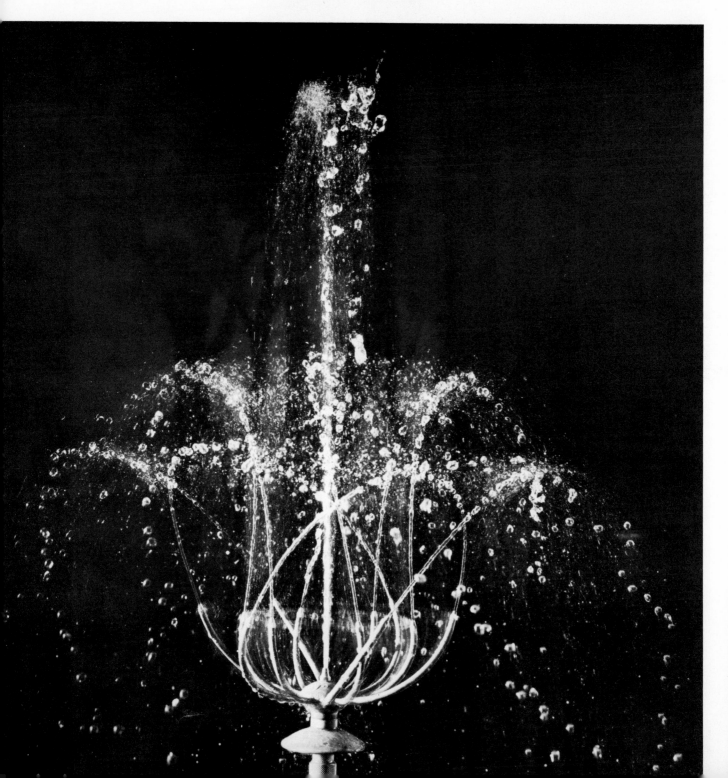

REGULARLY, in our everyday idiom, we pay lip service to some characteristic quirk of liquids. We describe a touch-and-go international situation as "fluid." We talk of "pouring oil on troubled waters." We decry people and events as "slower than molasses." Using such phrases, we are unaware, for the most part, that they rest on a thoroughly scientific base.

Matter in its liquid state is both commonplace and contrary. Liquids are in between gases and solids, and, as often with the middle child in a family, display an uneasy duality. In their most untrammeled moods, they are just as much on the go as gases, flow almost as readily, and are about as disorderly and as shapeless. On the other hand they do, when contained, retain a shape as distinct as a solid's; they are usually as tightly packed, and they have a definable size which cannot be compressed.

Another contradiction of liquids is that they are simultaneously abundant and rare in nature. Water, the basic liquid, covers three fourths of the earth's surface, and makes up 60 per cent of the weight of our bodies. Yet water and petroleum—which is stored in the earth's crust—are the only two liquids which occur freely in nature. Occasionally a volcano on a rampage spews forth molten lava. There are, as well, certain organic fluids, themselves largely composed of water: those in our bodies, including blood, the sap of trees and plants—the sugary variety of maples, the resin from pines—and the oil of olives, peanuts, cottonseed. Of more than fourscore elements occurring in nature, only two are liquid. One is mercury, the skittish stuff of barometers; the other is bromine, the fuming, reddish-brown fluid which, in compound form, helps sedate our nerves. Mercury and bromine, indeed, underscore the rarity of natural liquids; they never appear solo in nature, only in concert with other substances.

Most of the liquids in the world today are creatures of man's own ingenuity: vegetable oil, alcohol, gasoline, glycerine, glycol, acetone and others. Their varieties and uses are legion, ranging from the synthetic cleansing agents known as detergents to the automobile antifreeze, ethylene glycol.

In addition to all the basic liquids, there are liquid mixtures. These are of three types: solutions, in which the dissolved substance disappears; suspensions, in which the particles eventually settle out, and colloidal dispersions, in which the particles, though invisible to the eye, maintain their separate identity. Household ammonia—ammonia gas dissolved in water—is a solution; calamine lotion is a suspension. Among the kinds of colloid are a *gel*, or solid-in-liquid (gelatin, for instance); a *sol*, or less cohesive solid-in-liquid (milk of magnesia is one); and a variety of sol called an *emulsion*, or liquid-in-liquid, in which, usually, the components revert to their original state unless joined by a "stabilizer." Oil and water will stay emulsified if, for instance, soap is added, and

MATTER'S MOST PLAYFUL MOOD
The flowery pattern of this playing fountain *(opposite)* shows the controllable fluidity of matter in its liquid state. The molecules of a solid are too closely packed and tightly chained together—those of a gas too far apart and footloose—to permit such graceful stylized capers.

73

MOLECULAR MOTION AND THE STATE WATER IS IN

Of all substances on earth, only water is familiar to man in all three physical states —gas, liquid and solid. In any state, water molecules still consist of one atom of oxygen and two atoms of hydrogen, the familiar chemical formula H_2O. But as the state changes, so does molecular behavior, as shown in diagrams below.

CHAOS IN STEAM

In this model of molecules in steam, the large ball is an oxygen atom; the small balls are hydrogen. In gas, molecules are widely spaced, dart rapidly and collide with one another.

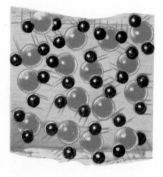

FLOW IN LIQUID

In liquid form, water molecules are close together, yet freely slip over one another, giving liquid its flow. This motion is more restricted than in gases, freer than in solids.

RIGIDITY IN ICE

In solid form, water molecules remain rigidly in place, held by forces of mutual attraction. When frozen, molecules form in hollow rings (as shown), giving ice its low density.

oil and vinegar only if egg yolk is added (thereby forming mayonnaise).

The man who formally identified the colloid—and named it after the Greek word for glue—was a 19th Century Scottish chemist, Thomas Graham, who came upon it while investigating the diffusion of liquids. Relatively few scientists are associated primarily with the study of liquids; most of our knowledge about them has been advanced through the study of gases. Graham, in addition to his laboratory studies, is also remembered for having recommended that ethyl alcohol, when sold tax-free for scientific purposes, be made undrinkable by the addition of poisonous "wood-spirit" (wood alcohol)—a move appreciated by the scientist if not by the toper.

A tiny world with the jitters

Whether in its pristine state, in solution or colloidal, a liquid is motivated, as are gases and solids, by the nature and behavior of its molecules. The molecules of a gas, as we have seen in the preceding chapter, are spaced relatively far apart; ruggedly individualistic, their interaction with each other—except when they collide—is almost negligible. A solid, on the other hand, is a close-knit, highly structured society whose molecules are steadfastly cooperative. Molecules in liquids, like those in gases, are in incessant motion, yet at the same time almost always as closely packed as the molecules of a solid. The effect is that of infinitesimally small ball bearings, rolling and slipping around each other—a shifting, jostling world in continuous nervous contact, with independent aims but imposed cohesiveness.

Among the major forces holding the molecules of liquids together are the same Van der Waals variety that, as noted in Chapter 3, cause attraction between the molecules of gas; in fact, these forces are what largely determine whether a substance is going to be a gas, liquid or indeed a solid. The Dutch physicist Johannes Diderik van der Waals hypothesized their existence in 1873 to account for certain odd behavior in a gas, but he did not explain their origin. This remained to be done by a later generation of scientists.

As they explained it, these forces of attraction come about as follows. Electrons which orbit atomic nuclei occasionally bunch up at one side, creating a temporary preponderance, on that side, of a negative electric charge. This charge is matched by an equal positive charge on the other side, created by the departure from it of the aforesaid electrons. The atom in question is thus "polarized"—that is, it has positive and negative charges at opposite ends. Since liquid molecules lie in close contact with one another, the polarity in one can displace the electrons in the near side of its neighbors, polarizing them as well. Oppositely charged sides of temporarily polar particles momentarily attract one another.

The Van der Waals forces, however, are not quite the whole story of binding in liquids. In the particular and supremely important case of water, another more powerful binding is also at work; it accounts for most of water's unexpected properties. A water molecule comprises one atom of oxygen and two atoms of hydrogen. The two hydrogen atoms, sticking out of the molecule like rabbit's ears, are in themselves enormously active, charged bodies which grab at and hold on to the oxygen atom of other water molecules. This makes for even stronger bonds among the molecules than the attraction involved in the Van der Waals forces. As will be detailed later, the "hydrogen bond" is largely responsible for the unexpectedly high freezing and boiling points of water, its unusual cohesiveness and the unique way in which it wets some substances.

If the temperature of a liquid goes high enough, no force can prevent its molecules from flying apart; it thus becomes a gas. If the temperature goes low enough, the molecules of a liquid will be drawn into rigid alignment so that they can no longer slide about one another; thus the liquid becomes a solid. One liquid alone has never been solidified under normal atmospheric pressure: liquid helium, which below a certain temperature becomes a "superfluid" known as helium II. This remarkable liquid defies the downward pull of gravity to creep up along the sides of its container and over the edges, and is also an extraordinary conductor of heat—about 200 times better than solid copper. The unique performance of helium II has startled and intrigued scientists, and research into its mysteries continues.

The properties of other liquids, however, are known to be determined by the behavior patterns of their particular molecules. The degree of attraction between layers of these molecules, for example, regulates the most obvious characteristic of a liquid—its ability to flow. The more its molecules are drawn together, the greater the internal friction in the liquid; hence the greater resistance to flow. This resistance, or viscosity, was defined by Isaac Newton three centuries ago in his *Principia* as a "want of lubricity." It is apparent in molasses (hence the term "slower than molasses") and also in heavy oil; we recognize this property in a practical way when we switch to the use of a thicker lubricating oil in our automobiles in the summertime, since viscosity tends to decrease with rising temperatures.

A flair for the lowest level

While heavy oil and molasses move sluggishly, gasoline flows easily. Water, though it has more internal resistance than gasoline, sufficiently responds to the pull of the earth's gravity so that it moves "downhill" through thousands of miles from a sprawling network of little streams and brooks into a huge river like the Mississippi. Indeed, water's perpet-

THREE TIES THAT BIND

The uncommon qualities of our commonest liquid, water—its surface tension, adhesion, high boiling point—depend on a trio of forces, one within the molecule and two between adjoining molecules.
● Covalent bonds link atoms into molecules by means of shared electrons. In water, the two hydrogen nuclei *(small plus signs)* are held at a 105° angle, thus keeping one side of the molecule positive, the other negative.
● Hydrogen bonds are strong electrical linkages between the plus charges of the hydrogen nuclei and certain negative electrons of nearby atoms.
● Van der Waals forces are weaker electrical links between an oxygen nucleus and electrons of a nearby oxygen atom.

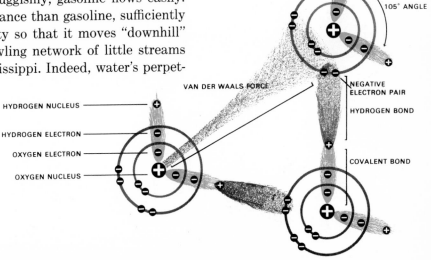

105° ANGLE

VAN DER WAALS FORCE

NEGATIVE ELECTRON PAIR

HYDROGEN BOND

COVALENT BOND

HYDROGEN NUCLEUS

HYDROGEN ELECTRON

OXYGEN ELECTRON

OXYGEN NUCLEUS

THE POWERFUL PRESSURES THAT SHAPE WATERDROPS

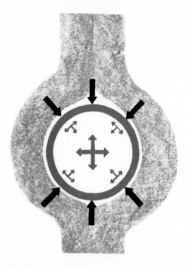

BALANCED FORCES IN FOG

The cohesion of water molecules in the surface of the fog drop above creates an elasticlike tension *(three-pronged arrows)* pushing from exterior to center. Air pressure also presses from outside *(black arrows)*. Pushing against the surface from inside is hydrostatic pressure *(blue arrow)*, which acts to rupture the drop. Air pressure and surface tension holding the drop together equal the disruptive force of hydrostatic pressure; since all forces press on the drop's surface equally, it is spherical.

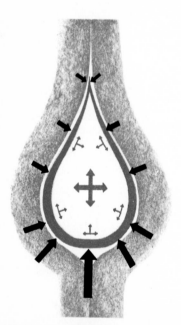

UNEQUAL STRESSES IN RAIN

Unlike a fog drop, which is tiny, light and sinks slowly toward the earth, a larger, heavier raindrop *(above)* is more strongly affected by the force of gravity and falls quickly. In falling, the balance of surface tension, hydrostatic pressure and air pressure that would make it a sphere is upset. The strongest air pressure is exerted directly underneath the drop *(heavy black arrow)* and gradually diminishes toward the top. This variation in air pressure gives a small raindrop its pear-shaped form.

ual tendency to seek the lowest possible level creates these waterways.

The mutual attraction of molecules, causing them to cluster together, is responsible for other crucial characteristics of a liquid. One is that its volume remains the same whether it is poured into a small glass or a big jug (gases, on the other hand, obligingly expand to fit the container concerned). And in their togetherness, the liquid molecules strongly resist the attempt to reduce this volume even under pressure. Rather than shrink, the liquid transmits such pressure evenly, without any gain or loss in force, to every part of the vessel in which it is contained. The science of hydraulics (from the Greek for "water" and "pipe") is based on this principle and on another enunciated by the great 17th Century intellectual wizard, Blaise Pascal: that a small exertion of pressure exerts multiples of its own force.

In his *Treatise on the Equilibrium of Liquids*, Pascal discussed a "new kind of machine to multiply forces," describing an experiment he had performed: "If a vessel full of water, closed on all sides, has two openings, one a hundred times larger than the other, with a piston carefully fitted to each, a man pressing the small piston will match the strength of a hundred men pressing the piston in the hundredfold greater opening, and will overmaster ninety-nine."

Powerhouse in a finger tip

Today we see the application of these principles of hydraulics when a touch of the foot applies the brakes in an automobile, and a finger tip's exertion controls power steering. With a suitable system of cylinders and pistons for applying pressure, engineers can design jacks and lifts for raising all manner of heavy objects, huge presses for stamping out metal parts, a thousand different actuators of the mechanisms of equipment.

While refusing to submit to pressure, a liquid will, on the other hand, amiably accept suggestions as to its shape. Lacking a characteristic conformation of its own, it will, when poured into a container, instantly assume the outline of the bottom of the container—this because it always seeks the lowest possible level. There is one notable exception to the rule. If the amount of liquid is very small, it does, indeed, take a shape of its own—as a droplet, a perfect example in miniature of the inward tug exerted by a liquid's interior molecules on those at the surface. The resulting shape is roughly spherical; both air pressure and the pull of gravity tend to distort it. (At "zero gravity," as orbiting astronauts have learned, drops of water assume the form of a perfect sphere.)

The droplet shape is also influenced by a unique characteristic of liquids called surface tension; this makes a liquid behave as though it were covered with an invisible elastic membrane which wants to contract and pull the liquid back into itself, making the least possible surface area. The

ETHER EVAPORATES IN BASE

tensile strength of the surface should be readily apparent to any man who has ever dropped a razor blade into a washbasin and seen it float.

A liquid's surface tension is caused simultaneously by the electrical attraction of the surface molecules for each other and the downward pull of those beneath them. For the weight of the molecules involved, the tension can be amazingly strong; in water, it has about the same tensile strength as that of structural steel.

The phenomenon of surface tension also figures, to some extent, in the celebrated ability of oil to calm troubled waters. This peculiar talent of oil—observed as long ago as the time of the Roman scholar Pliny, in the First Century A.D.—has not yet been completely explained by scientists. When a thin layer of a suitable oil is spread on the water, at least two mechanisms are at work. The lowered surface tension of the water tends to damp the movement of ripples or prevent them from forming. The clinging oil film acts as a membrane which resists the effort of the restless water to stretch or contract it. Both factors help the water present a smooth face to the wind, keeping larger waves from increasing in size and breaking at the crest.

The principle of the protective surface film has also been applied to help slow down the evaporation of water in arid regions of the Western states. In this case the substance used is a white, waxy, solid alcohol, hexadecanol (known as cetyl alcohol, and originally derived from the whale, but now made synthetically). Dusted on the surface of a reservoir and easily spread by a mild wind, it forms a clinging film one molecule thick—approximately six ten-millionths of an inch—which allows the passage of oxygen and other gases essential to aquatic life yet provides the water with a glassy surface. The film is harmless to human beings, fish and snakes, and self-healing when torn by rowboats, water skiers, rain and hail. Although not yet in wide-scale practical use, the hexadecanol coating has been proven by tests to retard water evaporation by as much as 25 per cent.

A propensity for outsiders

Strong as is the mutual molecular attraction which creates surface tension in liquids, an even stronger attraction exists—in the particular case of water—for outside molecules, as those in a solid which it adjoins. This propensity produces two other liquid phenomena of prime importance: wetness and capillarity.

Dropped on glass, mercury—whose molecules are more strongly tied to each other than water's—will haughtily bead up. Water, on the other hand, will cling slavishly to the glass, enamored of its molecules, spreading over it in a sheet, wetting it thoroughly; indeed "wetness" is this clinging capacity. This is one of the characteristics of water which is ex-

AN ETHERIZED OPERATION

This familiar bobbing toy operates by the evaporation of ether. The bird consists of two spheres connected by a long tube. Liquid ether, a substance which evaporates quickly at room temperature, is placed in the bottom sphere. It starts to vaporize (Figure 1), creating pressure (Figure 2, *small arrows*) pushing it up the tube. Ether collects in the upper sphere but does not vaporize because a covering on the head has been wet with cooling water. When ether in the top outweighs the quantity at the bottom, the bird pivots forward (Figure 3), permitting the ether to run back to the body (Figure 4). Each pivot moistens and cools the bird's head.

LIQUID RISES INTO HEAD   BIRD TILTS: ETHER FLOWS BACK   BIRD PIVOTS UPRIGHT AGAIN

plained by its hydrogen bonding. The nuclei of the hydrogen atoms in water form a strong tie with oxygen atoms in the silicon dioxide surface of the glass.

To be wet by water a glass surface must be clean; if it is spotted with even minute bits of oil or grease (usually present in dust particles which have come to roost), water's natural aversion to such substances will assert itself. In one notable instance, however, this aversion can be overcome; in solution with soap, water will "wet" even grease. This is effected by the two-faced behavior of the soap molecule. One end of it is attracted to the water molecule, the other end to the grease molecule. This it lures into the water, permitting the grease to be rinsed off at will. On such a simple strategem rests man's ability to present a clean countenance to the world.

Water's affinity for alien molecules is also seen in the phenomenon called capillarity. The molecules in the glaze of a cup, for example, will so attract the molecules of water poured into the cup that the water will rise slightly up the sides. A piece of fine glass tubing immersed in this same water will provide even more surface for the water molecules to disport on. They will try to pull themselves up the inside of the tube in a kind of hand-over-hand action. As the water climbs up, its surface tension tries to flatten it out; this in turn enables the water at the sides of the tube to climb even higher. These alternate activities continue until the liquid reaches a height at which the weight of its column balances the upward-directed force of the glass molecules.

The finer the bore of the tube—i.e., the smaller its inside diameter—the greater the water's capillarity; the word, in fact, derives from the Latin *capillus*, hair, emphasizing the slenderness of the channel up which the water moves. Capillarity draws liquids into all sorts of small spaces where they adhere, spread and crawl like ink on blotting paper. It helps towels wipe away water, and causes melted wax to continue feeding the flame of a candle. No process more vital than capillary action can be found in nature: it is what enables water to move through the soil toward the roots of plants.

Finale of an adventurer

The same restless adventurism which causes a liquid to climb, creep, flow and generally keep on the go results in its ultimate undoing: at certain temperatures it literally vanishes into vapor—gas. The process of vaporization accounts for the fact that there are so few liquids occurring in nature. It takes two forms: evaporation, in which only part of the surface liquid turns into gas, and boiling, in which all parts of the liquid turn into gas. Boiling, which takes place at higher temperatures, is thus an extreme case of evaporation.

The culprits responsible for the phenomenon of evaporation are, as in other instances of a liquid's curious behavior, the molecules at the surface of the liquid. These are a fickle lot by any standard. As mentioned earlier, they spend much of their time trying to get back into the interior of the liquid, under coaxing by their fellow molecules on the inside. On the other hand, when imbued with higher energy by some outside source of heat, and when faced in an outward direction, they willy-nilly break away from home, popping off into the atmosphere and turning into molecules of vapor. As more and more depart, the surface of the container—whether it be a glass jar or human skin—is bereft of their energy and drops in temperature (this explains why evaporation produces a cooling effect). In time the vapor above has had enough of these escape artists and will accept no more; at this point the air over the liquid is said to be "saturated," and the vapor "in equilibrium" with the liquid. Any more molecules leaving the liquid are offset by molecules going back, i.e., condensing, into the liquid. Thus evaporation is exactly counterbalanced by condensation.

The saturation of air is none other than the bugaboo of weather: humidity. Warmer air will absorb more vaporized water than cooler air. In humid weather, when the warm air is nearly saturated, our perspiration stops evaporating, and we swelter and feel oppressed. On the other hand, when humidity is low even intense heat is tolerable, because our perspiration evaporates easily, thus cooling the body.

The rise and fall of a bubble

The vapor formed above a liquid has its own kind of pressure, high when the surface tension of the liquid is low (as in the case of an extremely volatile fluid like household ammonia) and low when the surface tension is high (as in the case of water or acetic acid, the pungent ingredient of vinegar). As the temperature of the liquid is raised, its vapor pressure rises; when it equals the prevailing atmospheric pressure, the liquid reaches its boiling point. The vapor pressure is able to overcome the atmospheric pressure; the liquid loses its surface-tension barrier, and bubbles of vapor form in its interior, growing larger and larger, and violently agitate the entire liquid, causing it to boil away. Various liquids boil at various temperatures; their degree of reluctance to boil depends, in general, on how fond their particular molecules are of each other. Ether boils at 34.6°C. (94.3°F.); chloroform boils at 61.3°C. (142.3°F.); carbon tetrachloride at 76.8°C. (170.2°F.), and turpentine at 160°C. (320°F.). Water, with its high molecular attraction, boils at 100°C. (212°F.), expanding more than 1,500 times as it turns into saturated water vapor, or steam; it is this simple but irresistible expansion which drives a steam engine.

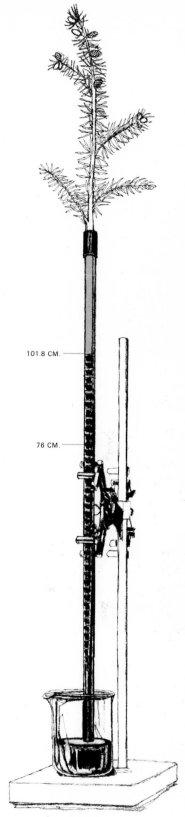

101.8 CM.

76 CM.

A MOLECULAR CHAIN GANG
Moisture rises to treetops because of a remarkable property called cohesion, by which water molecules hold onto one another like links in a chain. As the top water molecules in the chain evaporate from the leaf, more are pulled up from the roots through tiny ducts in the trunk. In this experiment a twig joined to a column of water and mercury lifts the mercury to 101.8 centimeters; normal air pressure would lift it only to 76 centimeters.

79

One of the greatest curiosities about water occurs at the climax of its heating process. To raise the temperature of a gram of water by 1°C. anywhere up to its boiling point requires the same amount of heat: one calorie for each degree. But when the same amount of water reaches its 100°C. boiling point, an extra kick of 540 calories is needed to convert it completely into vapor, i.e., to make it boil away. The lion's share of this extra heat is required simply to overcome the cohesive forces which bind water molecules together; in other words, the sturdy hydrogen bonds put up a terrific last-ditch fight against being rent asunder. It is this fact—that water takes such a high heat to vaporize—which is utilized in steam-heating systems.

A problem of raw potatoes

When the pressure on a liquid is lowered, its boiling point drops and —as anyone knows who has tangled with a batch of raw potatoes in the rarefied air of a mountaintop—food takes longer to cook. On the other hand, lowering the boiling point—with the corresponding reduction in temperature—has its advantages; certain foods which might be injured at high temperatures yield up their water content happily at low pressures; vacuum techniques used in the commercial processing of orange juice, for example, remove most of the water and allow the concentrated juice to be frozen and packaged without deterioration of the vitamin content and flavor.

Similar benefits to the appetite accrue when the pressure on a liquid is increased and its boiling point rises; the elevation in temperature promotes very rapid cooking. This is the principle of the pressure cooker, a utensil not as new to history as is generally supposed. The first of its kind, known as "Papin's pot," was invented in Germany around 1680 by a French physician, natural philosopher and mechanic, Denis Papin, who had had to leave his native land because of the persecution of Protestants after the revocation of the Edict of Nantes. Vastly intrigued by the behavior of water under pressure, Papin conducted numerous experiments on vaporization. He invented the safety valve and helped develop the steam engine. Such an engine, the story goes, went into a paddlewheel boat which he built; the water raised by the engine fell on the wheels and turned them. When Papin tried, however, to give his craft a shakedown cruise on a German river, he became one of the first recorded victims of the laboring man's ire against automation; en route the boat was wrecked by angry bargemen.

In the centuries since Papin, plain ordinary water has lost none of its fascination for the scientists. Colorless, odorless, tasteless, taken completely for granted in everyday life, it remains, to the men who have pondered its properties, the most remarkable liquid of them all—the

DINING UNDER PRESSURE
French physicist Denis Papin invented the first pressure cooker *(opposite)* in 1681 by applying the principle that a liquid's boiling point rises as air pressure increases. Thus under pressure water boils at higher than 212° F. and cooks food faster. Visiting England, Papin prepared a meal in his cooker for the Royal Society. It was described by diarist John Evelyn as "all dress'd, both fish and flesh, in Monsieur Papin's Digestors, by which the hardest bones of beefe and mutton were made soft as cheese."

inscrutable helium II notwithstanding. Many a lengthy treatise has been devoted to just one or another of its unique characteristics.

Water, for example, is the only substance which commonly exists in all three states of matter simultaneously—as solid, liquid and gas. Above a river covered with ice—water in its solid form—rises the vapor of water in its gaseous form; below the river's surface, water courses in its liquid form.

The span between water's freezing and boiling points (0° to 100°C., or 32° to 212°F.) is the most important range of temperature on our planet. In defining the limits within which water is in its liquid state, this span also defines the limits within which our bodies can function. For water is the essential constituent of all living things. The human body is a virtual walking sack of precariously contained fluids. Water is the chief substance of the living cell, which rose to its present state out of enriched sea water, and ever since departing this primordial home has had to carry its own sea water in the form of blood. Water also forms a smooth egg-white liquid, called "synovial fluid," that lubricates joints between bones and makes it possible for us to get around (we could not even walk across the room without it). Water's capacity to dissolve solids and gases and to hold colloids in suspension enables it to transport nourishment and oxygen.

In fact, we judge the possibility of life as we know it on other planets in terms of whether or not their temperatures would permit water to be liquid, and indeed whether they possess water at all. In our own solar system, this eliminates Mercury, whose temperatures are so enormously hot that lead would melt on its side closest to the sun. It eliminates Venus, which swelters in a dry heat hostile to life. Mars more closely resembles the earth, and traces of water appear to be present on it in polar icecaps, but possibly none in liquid form; even so, conditions on Mars might allow some simple form of life to arise. The other planets appear to be in such a deep freeze that the presence of water is extremely unlikely under any circumstances.

Gratitude on a planet

On our own beautiful blue-green planet we can thank water for the relatively temperate nature of our surroundings. On the whole, the earth has a gracious, moderate climate because of the tremendous heat-carrying ocean currents and water-carrying air currents that are always at work over the surface of the globe, reducing temperatures that are high, raising those that are low. This heat-transport mechanism would be less effective were it not for water's most curious property—unusual even in the unusual world of liquids.

When cooled, most well-behaved liquids shrink; at their freezing point

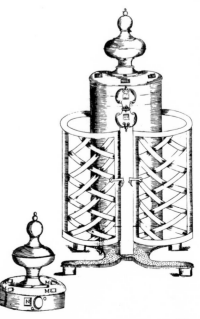

TO A KING'S TASTE
King Charles II of England, a scientific dilettante, ordered a "Digestor," as the first pressure cooker was called, from its inventor, Denis Papin (opposite). Perhaps mindful of his royal patron's safety, Papin produced the sturdy pot at right. The weighted lid, shown removed at left, is bolted firmly to the cooker. A metal screen surrounds the cooking chamber in case of explosion. Steam flows inside a central cylinder and around an inner pot, where the food is placed.

they are at their most dense, and too heavy to float. Water follows the conformist pattern until it gets down to four degrees above its freezing point. Then, suddenly, it kicks over the traces. Instead of continuing to shrink, it begins to expand and keeps on expanding until zero. (At that point, it undergoes another sharp expansion, thereby causing water pipes to burst.) The explanation for water's peculiar behavior lies in the activity of its molecules at the critical temperature of 4°C. Instead of pulling themselves closer together as the cold reduces their movement, they string themselves out along the lines of the hydrogen bonds between them. By the time zero is reached, they have formed a crystalline structure, but one that is airy and open and thus relatively lighter than water itself. In short, water in its frozen state—ice—is able to float on water in its liquid state.

This phenomenon accounts for the fact that the waters of the earth remain fluid throughout the winter, even though their surface may be blanketed with ice. Accordingly, with the coming of spring each year, it is relatively easy for the sun to warm the surface and melt the ice away. Without this unusual characteristic of water, the far northern and far southern reaches of the globe would freeze up solid, forever blocking the flow of ocean currents and leaving many parts of the earth with perhaps intolerable extremes of heat and cold. Thus life in the aggregate, no less than the lives of individuals, depends on the fortuitous ways of a liquid.

On the Surface, More Than Meets the Eye

To the uninitiated, the "surface" of an object is merely its outside—its top or its face. But to the scientist who is investigating matter, surfaces are indeed very special affairs, and are often possessed of very special properties. He calls them, more properly, "interfaces," for it is virtually impossible for one surface not to be in contact with another surface. Like a liquid layer cake, the colorful concoction opposite, a so-called pousse-café, abounds with interfaces (12 all together), where each liqueur touches other liqueurs (or glass)—except for the highest layer, whose top surface is an interface with air. Surfaces derive their importance primarily from the fact that many substances show markedly different characteristics along their surfaces than they do elsewhere. Surface phenomena are to be found everywhere—busily coloring the sky blue, contributing to the stiffness of crinoline and also accounting for the slipperiness of oil.

THE GRAVITY OF A DRINK
The six layers of liqueurs in a pousse-café (opposite), made by pouring successively lighter liqueurs on top of one another, are kept separate by the differences in their specific gravity, or weight relative to water (marked at left of the drink). However, the distinctive surfaces in this bartender's nightmare are very tenuous, since a jolt would blend all the components into a murky mixture.

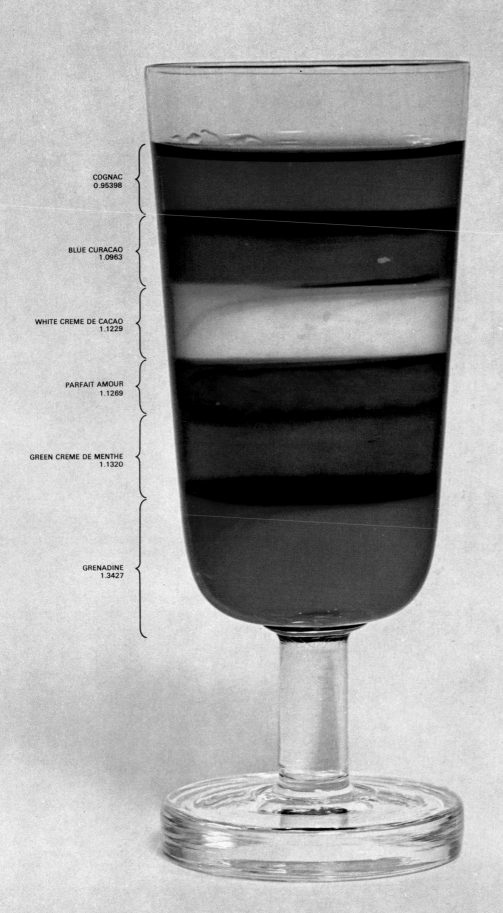

COGNAC
0.95398

BLUE CURACAO
1.0963

WHITE CREME DE CACAO
1.1229

PARFAIT AMOUR
1.1269

GREEN CREME DE MENTHE
1.1320

GRENADINE
1.3427

The Phenomena of Familiar Kitchen Concoctions

Everytime a housewife whips up any one of the concoctions shown here, she has a bowl of surface phenomena. For the ability of ingredients to mix and stay mixed is in large part a property of their surfaces.

The smaller any object gets, the more surface it has for its weight. A mouse has two square inches of skin per ounce; an elephant less than 1/25 square inch per ounce. There comes a point where the surface of a solid takes precedence over its volume and becomes a controlling factor in its behavior. An orange, for instance, will sink in water. Even the larger particles in orange juice settle out. But if the orange could be sufficiently fragmented, its individual particles would not sink. They would be kept up by the ceaseless motion of the molecules of water, as in an endless game of volleyball in which nobody drops the ball. Particles that are small enough have so much surface area exposed—in comparison with their infinitesimal weight —that they will be influenced by this molecular movement rather than by gravity. This condition is called a colloid, represented by the mayonnaise, gelatin and starch at right. When the solid particles are too big for the liquid molecules to support, the result is a "suspension" (the orange juice and cooky ingredients). In the third condition, a "solution," the molecules of the liquid and of the solid mix completely, as in sugar dissolved in tea.

A SUGARY SOLUTION

Sugar cubes, added to a cup of tea, produce a true solution—an intermingling of sugar and water which is indivisible by such mechanical means as filtering. For the components of the mixture to be separated, one of them must undergo a physical change—most easily accomplished in this case by simply boiling off the water into steam, leaving a residue of sugar.

A PULPY SUSPENSION

Although the average bleary-eyed breakfaster is unaware of it, his morning orange juice is, technically, a "suspension"—fragments of orange lolling about in water. At right, some particles have already settled to the bottom; the rest will join them eventually. Because the fragments are relatively big, they respond to the pull of gravity rather than molecular buoyancy.

A CLOSE-KNIT COLLOID

A dollop of mayonnaise atop the tomato salad above is a colloid called an emulsion—a mixture of immiscible (i.e., unmixable) liquids. Such a feat is made possible with the oil and vinegar ingredients of the mayonnaise by the gluing action of a "binder," in this case the yolk of egg, which holds a myriad of microscopic oil globules in a colloidal state within the vinegar.

A CRUMBLED MIXTURE
The scattered pecans below, when embedded in the wet dough or in the finished cookies, are in a state of suspension. But while they are part of the dry ingredients, they demonstrate a primary quality of a true mixture: the ability of the components to be separated mechanically. In a mixture, no chemical reaction takes place, and each ingredient retains its own properties.

A FLAVORSOME GEL
When powdered gelatin is mixed with hot water, it becomes a colloid which, when cooled, forms what is known as a "gel"—a solid composed of microscopic gelatin particles bonded together by a network of fibers. In the above gelatin, the strawberry coloring and flavor, together with sugar, form a solution within the gel. Capsule casings of drugs are also gels.

A STARCHY POLYMER
Mixing water and laundry starch, as any housewife knows, after a short cooking produces a gooey liquid which—when dry—can stiffen wing collars, among other things. The chemist's formal name for this goo is a "high polymer" (i.e., many-parted) colloid. The reason for its colloidal state is the giant size of the starch molecule, formed by a long string of atoms.

Nature's Neat Way with a Mixture

Colloids and suspensions can be made by man, as shown on the preceding pages, but they also occur with great frequency in nature. Evidence of naturally occurring colloids and suspensions is seen in the smoky haze below and in the colorful rainbow opposite. In the case of the haze, a pall of low-lying smoke forms a colloid which remains airborne because of the supporting action of air molecules. In the case of the rainbow, water droplets left in the air by a passing shower form a suspension which reflects the entire spectrum of sunlight.

The reaction of light on such natural phenomena is shown in the experiment photographed at the left. A tank containing a sulphur colloid is penetrated by a white light which, as it encounters the colloid's tiny particles, is scattered into the component colors of the spectrum. The same phenomenon accounts for the gold of the sunset or blue of the sky; these effects are achieved by dispersal of the yellow or blue portions of the spectrum as they collide with different-sized particles of air and dust in the earth's atmosphere.

A SCATTERING OF LIGHT
Three beams of white light, passing through a colloid of sulphur particles in a liquid, change to orange, pink and bluish-green. This phenomenon is the "Tyndall effect," discovered in 1869 by John Tyndall, the British physicist. Tyndall showed that light rays will be scattered into different colors by minute particles of matter of uniform size. The colors produced will depend on the size of the particles and also on the position of the viewer. The smaller the particles contained in the colloid, the shorter (and bluer) the wavelengths of the spectrum they will scatter.

A FOGGY AEROSOL
A combination of fog and smoke over the city of Santa Barbara, California, illustrates two mixtures common in nature. Fog is a suspension of water droplets which will eventually settle out of the air by their own weight. Smoke is an airborne colloid, which scientists call an aerosol. The whitish color produced by the combination is still another instance of the Tyndall phenomenon *(above)*. Since smoke and fog particles vary in size, sunlight which hits them scatters at random, producing all the colors of the spectrum. Seen together, they appear white.

A SPECTRAL SUSPENSION
The rainbow above has been produced by the action of sunlight on droplets of water which are in suspension in the air. As the sunlight enters each droplet, the separate colors of its spectrum are bent—refracted—through different angles. This refracted light is then reflected off the back of each individual droplet, through the air, to the eye of the observer. The larger the droplets, the more brilliant the rainbow. This Spanish farmer, plowing his field not far from the city of Madrid, stands at the "end" of the rainbow, fabled locale of the pot of gold.

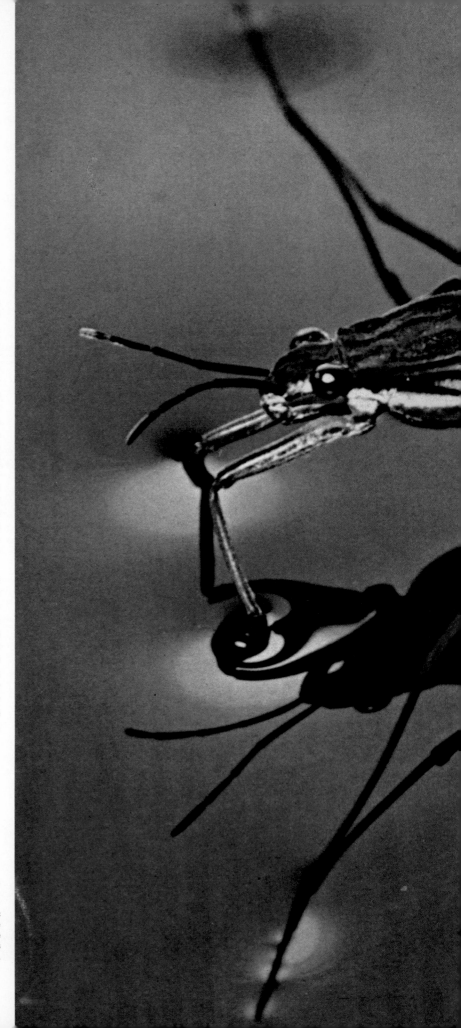

A Walk on Water with the Helping Hand of Molecules

The food-foraging quest of the minuscule bug at the right—a water strider shown magnified many times—illustrates the phenomenon of surface tension. This, in effect, coats the surface of a liquid with an invisible but entirely real elastic membrane—composed of the liquid's own molecules—which enables certain properly equipped bugs to traverse the surface with the confidence of a skater on solid ice. The phenomenon stems from the fact that the individual molecules within most liquids, and particularly water, are like the tiniest of magnets, radiating forces of attraction in every direction. Although they are forever in motion, these molecules are compulsively drawn to one another, so that the most contented molecule is the one completely surrounded by its fellows. But some molecules, perforce, must serve a temporary tour of duty on the surface of the liquid.

In the case of the water shown here, its surface molecules are exposed in some degree to air, for which their molecular attraction is slight at best. Thus, the pull on them is both downward (back amongst the other water molecules) and sideways (to their fellow surface molecules). The mutual attraction established between surface molecules is sufficiently strong for them to form a bond, almost as if they had linked arms. This accounts for the membranous quality of surface tension.

TIPTOE ON TENSION
Like several other insects, this water strider is especially endowed to take advantage of surface tension because of its wide weight distribution and hairy feet, which work like aquatic snowshoes. However, if it ever stood on one foot, the concentrated weight would penetrate the liquid molecular membrane which now holds it up—and it would undoubtedly get dunked.

Monolayers: Matter Spread Thin

What makes possible the watery walk of the bug on the previous page is a "monolayer"—a surface coating just one molecule thick. Technically this term can apply to any surface of matter. But usually scientists use it to describe the ultradiaphanous film formed by one substance on another kind of substance. By this definition the oil coating at right does not qualify; it is, relatively, as thick as an elephant hide. A true monolayer is seen opposite in the oily aroma of roses spread over a pool of mercury. The existence of a monolayer in the boiling oil below has not been proven one way or another.

Monolayers are much too thin to be seen except with an electron microscope. This fact and their general elusiveness make them intriguing to experimenters.

A SENSITIVE SURFACE
The orange-red image of the girl on the blue-green cake of ice above is registered on the oil-coated plastic membrane of an Evaporograph. This complex device measures the relative heat of objects by the effect of their infrared radiations on the oil coating. Color differences are caused by the varying thicknesses of the oil film in different states of evaporation from the surface.

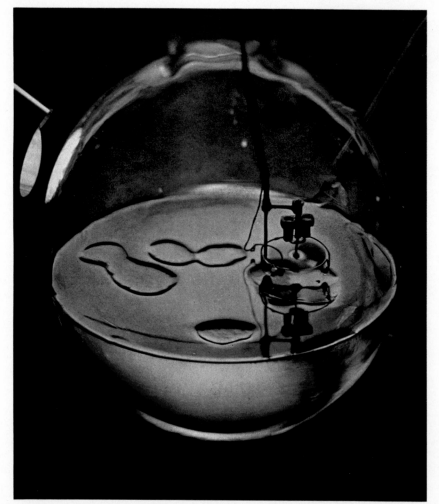

A PUZZLING IMPURITY
The oil boiling in a vacuum at left is a surface curiosity thought to be caused by a monolayer. Theoretically, the whole surface should be pocked by craterlike eruptions. But here these are relatively few in number. It is believed that impurities boiled out of the oil rain back onto the surface to form a monolayer which prevents the liquid from immediately boiling away.

A SCENT IN ACTION
The oily perfume from the two roses forms the swirl opposite. The pattern, shown covering a mercury surface with a monolayer of oil, is created when the oil pushes aside a powder coating. Mercury provides a supersmooth base for this demonstration because, in direct antithesis to oil, it has the greatest surface tension of any liquid. It also gives the swirl its slate-blue color.

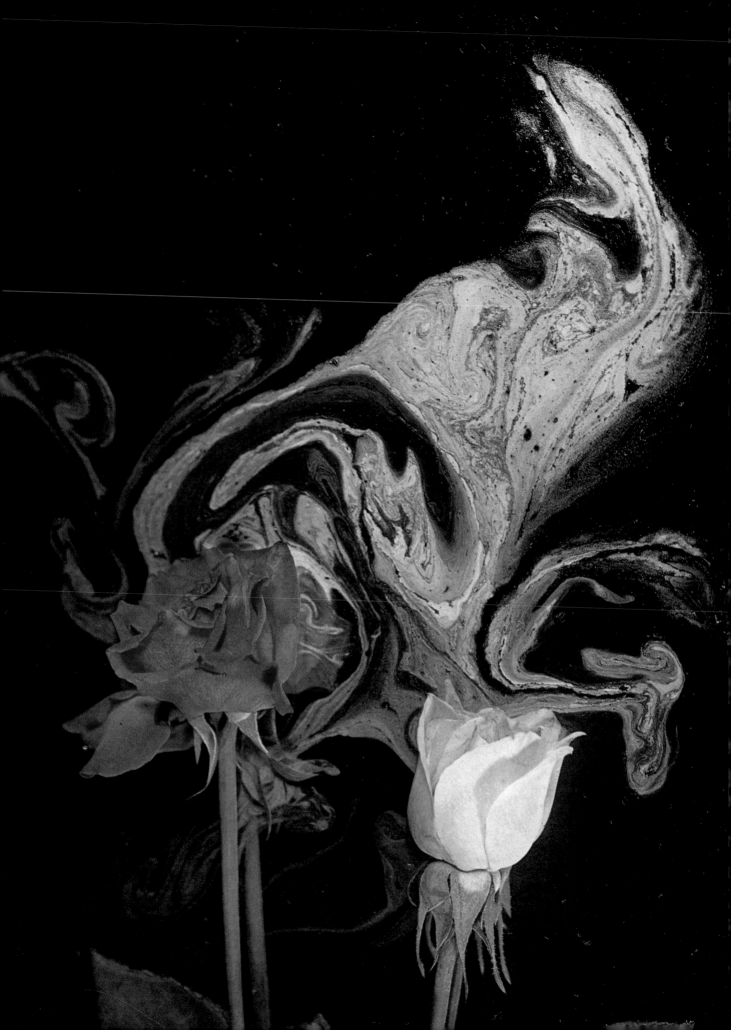

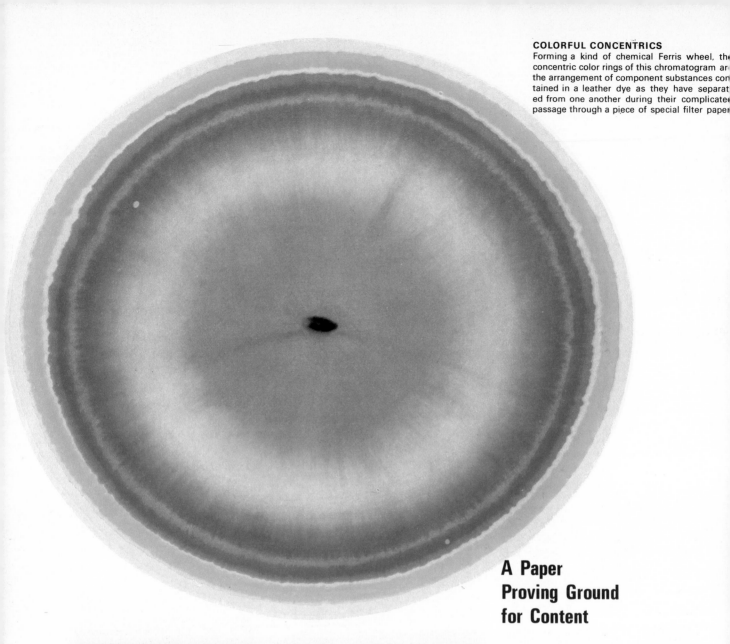

A Paper Proving Ground for Content

An ingenious tool for the chemist who must sort out the constituents of complex chemical solutions is the process shown on these pages. Called paper chromatography (color writing), it makes use of two surface phenomena. The first is adsorption (notice the "d")—the mutual attraction between surface molecules of liquids and solids; adsorption makes oil climb a kerosene lampwick. The second is the ease with which a chemical dissolves in a liquid—the way salt, for instance, takes to water, but shows little taste for alcohol.

In one method of paper chromatography, a solution being analyzed is dropped onto the center of a round filter paper, wet with another liquid. The ingredients of the solution tested creep outward, hurrying or lagging according to (1) their own adsorptive passion for the paper or (2) their ability to duck in and out of solution with the original solvent and with the liquid on the paper. The result is a bull's-eye separation of the ingredients, like the one above.

SOME TELLTALE DISKS
At a bench festooned with chromatograms, a Du Pont laboratory technician checks the strength of a synthetic dye. The various color bands on each chromatogram are the actual characteristic shades of individual compounds separated out of the particular solution analyzed. In the end it is color which enables the chroma-tographer to distinguish the individual components of a solution. Dyes are particularly suited to chromatography, but the technique can also be used with colorless solutions *(opposite)*. The process of chromatography dates from 1903, when a Russian botanist, M. S. Tswett, first used it in connection with a study of plant pigments.

92

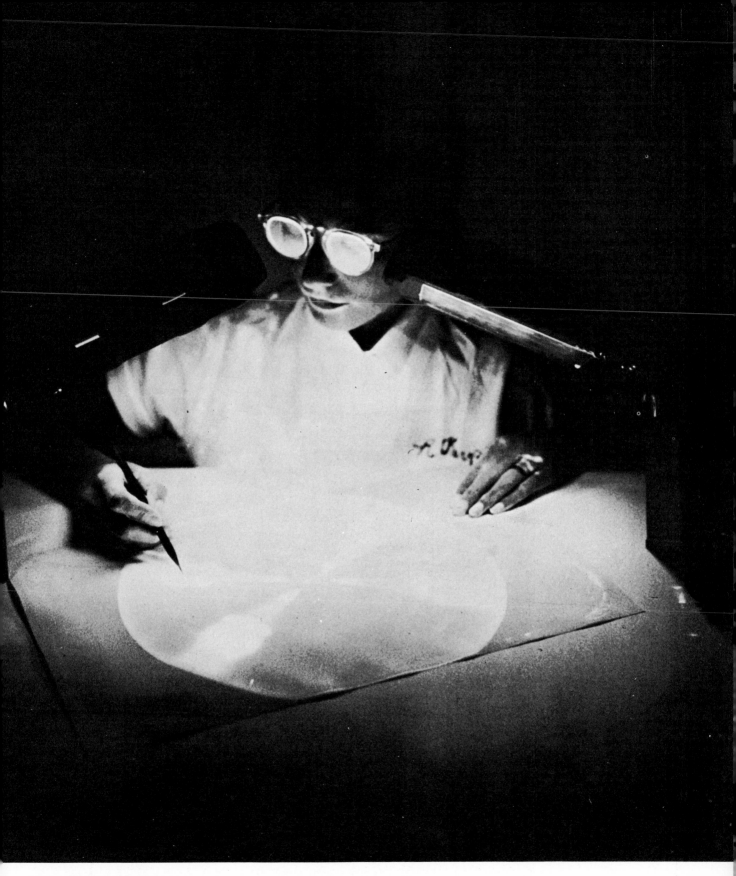

SCRUTINY OF A SOLUTION

An analyst checks the results of a chromatography test under the eerie glow of an ultraviolet lamp. This technique is often essential in the analysis of solutions which in ordinary light are colorless, or nearly so. In such cases, ultraviolet light is used, since many substances take on a distinctive shading in its rays. Many paper chromatography tests are made with the test solution applied to the center of the paper, from which the components separate out into a bull's-eye pattern *(opposite)*. In the case above, however, the solution was applied instead at four points on a square sheet of filter paper. This test involved the analysis of a drug solution.

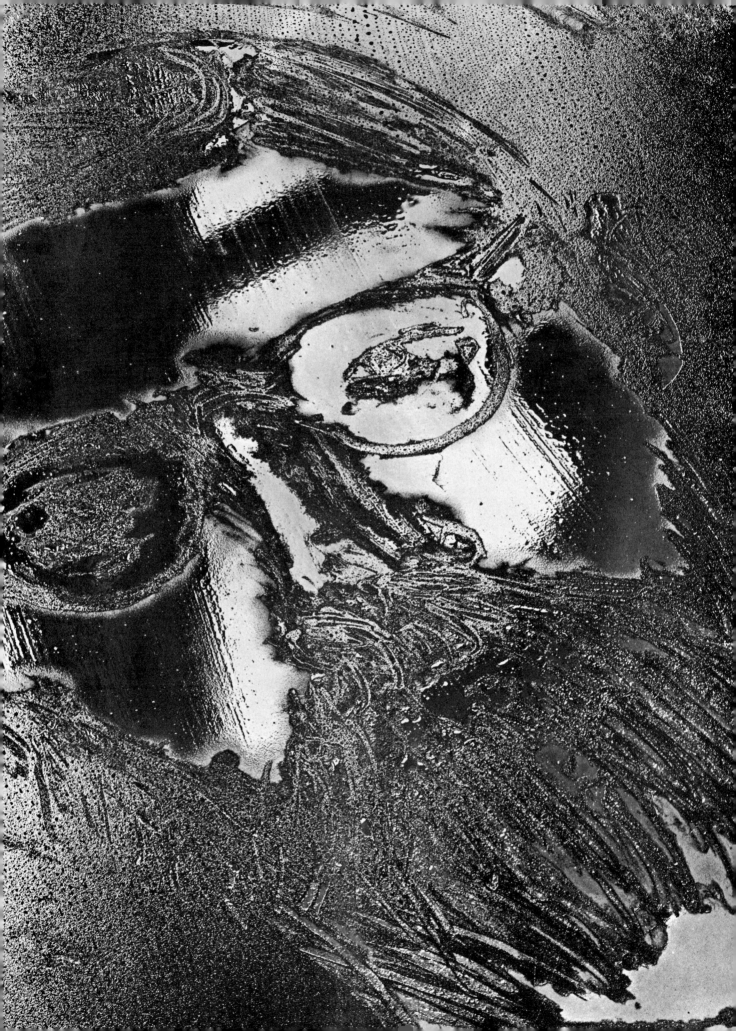

The Benefits of an Ancient Case of Incompatibility

The words "oil and water" instantly conjure up a picture of incompatibility: few substances are harder to mix. Although oil is commonly blamed for this state of affairs, the culprit is almost always water, which, because of the intense attraction between its own molecules, is near-narcissistic in its fondness for itself—so much so that it actually repels oil. A practical application of this surface phenomenon —and working proof that the oil-water feud can be fruitful—is seen in the lithographic process shown here. A greasy image drawn on stone is wetted with water, which withdraws from the grease onto the bare stone. Oily ink applied to the wetted surface with a roller is repelled by the water. Thus the ink adheres only to the greasy image, permitting it to be transferred to the paper to make a print.

RECEPTION IN LIMESTONE
One reason limestone is used in lithography is that it provides a surface readily wetted by water, an attraction seen in the close-up *(opposite)* of the plate being prepared at the right. On the greasy areas of the stone, water beads up; but on the bare areas it forms a shiny film. Ink then rolled onto the plate sticks only to the grease, enabling the image to be reproduced.

A PORTRAIT'S LAUNCHING
In the first step of lithography, artist Robert Parker of Carmel, New York, draws a portrait on limestone, using a greasy lithographic crayon.

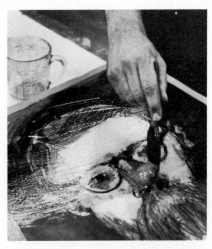

A LITHOGRAPHER'S TASK
The drawing completed, lithographer Arnold Singer applies a gum arabic and nitric acid solution to enhance the stone's attraction for water.

AN INVISIBLE IMAGE
The surface is cleaned with turpentine to remove all the excess grease. At this point, the image is impregnated into the surface of the stone.

AN APPLICATION OF WATER
Singer next wets the surface of the limestone with water, which retreats from the greasy image but still clings to the rest of the stone.

AN INKY REJECTION
Oily lithographic ink is rolled onto the entire stone, but the wetted surface rejects the ink, and the ink sticks only to the greasy drawing.

THE FINISHED PRODUCT
Singer peels off the finished print, a self-portrait of artist Parker. Thousands of copies can be made from the same plate. The paper in the process shown here is slightly damp but soon dries out. Commercial lithography uses metal plates but employs much the same technique.

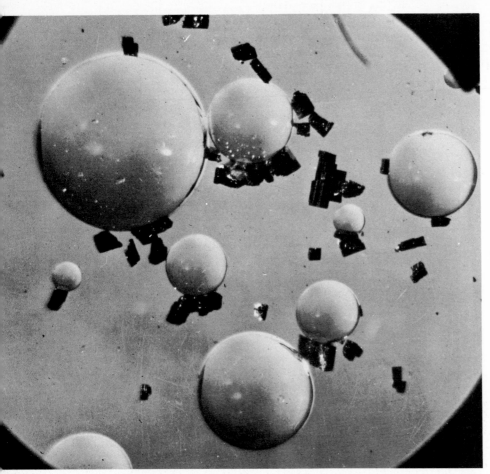

A DILEMMA OF FEATHERS
The madly paddling duck opposite is learning how it feels not to be able to stay afloat. Normally buoyed up by the water-repellent oil in its feathers, the duck has lost that protection through the application of a detergent—the same grease remover familiar to every kitchen.

The Fickle, Fluctuating Ways of Water

Water has a split personality: it has an innate penchant for attracting some substances and repelling others. However, chemical means can be used to induce a substance to reverse its normal reaction to water. The naturally oily feathers of the duck opposite are normally repelled by water, and this is the secret of the duck's usual success in staying topside. But application of a detergent allows the feathers to be "wetted"—and the duck begins to sink. Metal ores *(left)* ordinarily approve of water; but this feeling changes when a special chemical is mixed with the crushed ore in water. When air is injected, the ore promptly rides along with the resulting bubbles on their trip to the surface.

RESCUE ON A RAFT
Dark particles of galena, the ore from which most lead is refined, are affixed to air bubbles in this photomicrograph showing how the flotation process with ore occurs. Normally the galena would be wetted by water, but when xanthate, a chemical salt, is added, galena loses its tolerance for water. When air is piped into the bottom of the flotation tank, the xanthate-coated galena particles "raft" to the surface on air bubbles in their effort to leave the water.

FROTH AND FLOTATION
A trainload of copper ore *(above)* leaves an open pit mine on the way to the mill for refining. One of the early procedures after the ore has been ground is its removal from other substances, frequently by means of a flotation cell *(right)*. Here the frothy, ore-coated bubbles are skimmed from the surface. Often two or more flotations, involving different varieties of chemicals, are needed to recover all the copper.

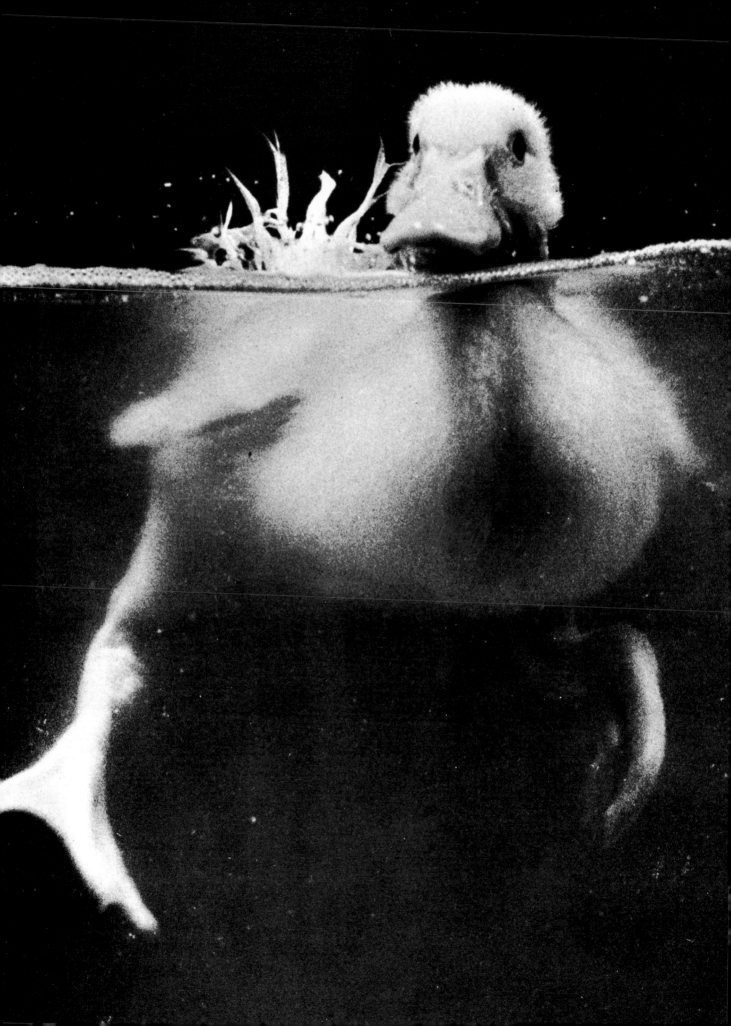

5

A Deceptive
Façade
of Solidity

By EVERY canon of common sense, the solid should have been the easiest form of matter for man to learn to know. Unlike the gas, it makes its presence plain; unlike the liquid, it stays readily in hand. Firm, compact, cohesive, it is by far the most satisfying to deal with. The inventory of solids began with the earliest cave man's earliest rock, and across the ages the list has lengthened without pause. Yet, astonishingly, it was not until 50 years ago that the actual structure of the solid was confirmed beyond a doubt.

Until this breakthrough, it was thought that the *content* of a solid was what determined its characteristics: what made diamonds hard, leather tough, iron magnetic and copper conductive. Vary the content and you could change the substance, said the classical chemists; add the right this and that and you would have a new substance totally different from the original. Today we know that many of the properties of a solid are determined by its *structure:* by the way the material's basic building blocks—its atoms—are ordered, and by the way they join together. We also know that what primarily distinguishes a solid from a liquid or a gas—what makes it seem rigid by comparison—is the arrangement and the relative closeness of its atom groupings, the molecules.

The shift in interest from the content to the form of a solid has caused a spectacular spurt in man's progressive conquest of his physical environment. From being a mere finder and assembler of materials, he has become a maker of them, a genuine architect of matter. He has gone into his laboratories and fashioned diamonds from peanut butter, silk from coal; he has even shaped an acceptable silk purse from genuine sow's ears. Many of the laboratories themselves have acquired a different look, far from the layman's concept of a domain cluttered merely with test tubes and retorts. To complement the scientist's present preoccupation with the three-dimensional structure of things, his workshops are filled with three-dimensional models of wire, wood and plastic—rambling, convoluted cylinders and hemispheres, and devices with knobby corners connected by rods, much like the toys in any well-equipped child's playroom. Studying these forms, working variations on them, researchers strive for a better intuitive grasp of how the properties of a material emerge from its structure.

On the long road to understanding the solid, certain milestones are especially noteworthy. The first was the realization, near the turn of the 19th Century, that many solids—and not just the translucent variety—are composed of crystals. (Among the exceptions: organic pitch, volcanic glass and opal.) The second was the emergence, toward the end of the century, of modern atomic theory, which showed that the crystal itself was made up of a particular arrangement of atoms. The third was the belated recognition, in 1912, that the interior of a solid could be scruti-

A PATTERN FOR BEAUTY
A diamond cutter must be an expert on crystalline structure, a characteristic of most solids. The black markings on the 726-carat Vargas diamond *(opposite)* indicate to the cutter the "grain" of the gem, the natural lines of cleavage where it must be cut. Although nature cannot make a more orderly crystal, every diamond has irregularities which could cause it to shatter in inexpert hands, making gem cutting a highly scientific—and ulcer-producing—line of work.

nized through the marvelous instrumentality of the X-ray, which had been discovered 17 years before. Thus utilized, the X-ray confirmed the picture of the solid as a neat mosaic of tiny crystals.

The pioneers of crystallography predated the 19th Century; in fact, many of their most pointed observations were made concurrently with the proclamations of 17th and 18th Century chemists that content was the key to a solid's properties. The early investigators began with the kinds of crystal that still commonly conjure up the name today: the symmetrical, show-through varieties seen in rock salt, snowflakes, diamonds, quartz and other minerals.

In the late 1660s Erasmus Bartholin, member of a remarkable Danish family of scholars and himself triply talented in mathematics, physics and medicine, received from Iceland some samples of crystals of calcite —a mineral known today as calcium carbonate, then called Iceland spar. Large transparent crystals of minerals are fairly rare in nature, and the calcite discovery had stirred unusual attention. Studying the crystals, Bartholin noted a "wonderful and extraordinary phenomenon": calcite had the property of double refraction, that is, objects viewed through it appeared double, whereas if they had been seen through other transparent bodies they would have appeared as a single refracted image. In 1669 another versatile Dane, Nicolaus Steno, set forth what is now called "the first law of crystallography." Steno, a physician, professor of anatomy and cleric (he subsequently became a Lutheran bishop), found in studying different quartz crystals that each had precisely identical angles between its corresponding faces; this similarity was later found to hold between crystals of other substances.

Fragments of a lucky break

The most brilliant intuitive deduction about the true nature of crystals was made by the Abbé René Just Haüy, a professor of humanities at the University of Paris. A lucky mishap led him to it; while examining a group of calcite crystals in a friend's collection in 1781, he dropped one of the larger ones. It not only broke in fragments but, to Haüy's great interest, it also broke along distinctive straight-line planes. Although gem cutters had long known of this phenomenon of cleavage, it set Haüy's mind busily to work. The "preferred cleavage planes" along which crystals split led him to surmise that the regular external form of crystals was a reflection of some kind of inner regularity—and that this must be due to some regularity of arrangement of constituent building blocks. At the time the existence of such building blocks—or atoms —was still a matter of great controversy. Haüy, however, concluded that a crystal was built up by the stacking of some kind of building blocks in parallel layers. From this he deduced that the angles in the crystal

REWARD FOR A CLASSIC DISCOVERY
This Nobel Prize certificate, together with a medal and $13,400, was presented to the German scientist Wilhelm Conrad Roentgen in Stockholm, Sweden, on November 12, 1901 —the first Nobel Prize for physics. The award was made for his discovery of X-rays in 1895; Vienna hospitals began using the new radiation for presurgical examination a few weeks after Roentgen's epochal finding.

would therefore be determined by the whole-number ratios in which the unsplittable building blocks were laid down along the crystal's sides. On this basis he enunciated the "law of rational intercepts."

With this tantalizing hint of some kind of mysterious architecture existing within solids, crystallography drew growing attention through the early part of the 19th Century. Using cleavage-plane analysis and microscopes, investigators gradually arrived at the startling realization that with certain exceptions most solids are crystals. They also concluded that in all of nature's copious bounty of solid materials, there are only seven major divisions of crystals (illustrated in the margin on page 106), which are classified according to their geometrical symmetries as follows:

	Division	Examples
(1)	Cubic	*Diamond, alum, gold, iron, lead, copper, silver*
(2)	Tetragonal	*Tin, zircon, rutile, scheelite*
(3)	Rhombic	*Topaz, sulphur, iodine, silver nitrate*
(4)	Monoclinic	*Borax, cane sugar, gypsum*
(5)	Triclinic	*Copper sulphate, boric acid*
(6)	Trigonal	*Arsenic, quartz, ice, graphite*
(7)	Hexagonal	*Magnesium, zinc, beryllium, cadmium, calcium*

Within these seven major "systems" are 32 subcategories, mathematically determined by the possible number of ways in which the symmetrical arrangements of groups of atoms can occur.

However substantial, the knowledge accumulated by early crystallographers was based on no more than careful reasoning, from external appearances, as to what the interior of solids was really like. Their work might have remained little but inspired guessing had it not been for a technique that permitted man to look into the heart of solid materials and actually see the artful placement of atoms; this technique was born of one of the most significant accidents in scientific history.

In late 1895, in his laboratory at the University of Würzburg, a tall and taciturn German physicist named Wilhelm Conrad Roentgen was studying the behavior of a contemporary electrical curiosity called a "Crookes tube." In the course of an experiment late one afternoon, he covered the tube with a jacket of black paper, making it immune to light, then pulled down the window shade and slipped the high-voltage switch to make doubly sure that no light was leaking from the tube. Suddenly, out of the corner of his eye, he caught a greenish glow from a nearby bench. When he turned off the tube, the glow disappeared. He struck a match and peered at the bench. There lay a square of cardboard which Roentgen, in connection with a totally different experiment, had

AN X-RAY TOOL FOR CRYSTAL GAZING

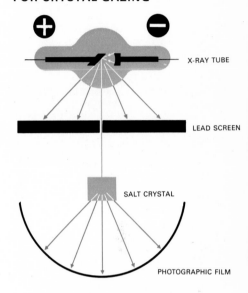

SEEING SALT'S SPOTTY SKELETON
The spotty photograph of salt below is a product of the X-ray diffraction process diagrammed above, the physicist's classic tool in the study of crystals. Rays from the X-ray tube are blocked by the lead screen except where a small hole allows a pencil beam of rays to hit the crystal of sodium chloride (common table salt). The radiation that penetrates the crystal to the photographic film makes the pattern below. The big white spot in the center is the main unscattered beam of X-rays. The size and arrangement of the other spots result from the bouncing around of the rays in the latticework structure of the sodium and chlorine atoms in the crystal. Every crystalline substance has a unique X-ray diffraction picture. A sodium chloride crystal will always produce this same design.

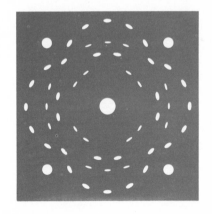

coated with crystals of barium platinocyanide, a fluorescent substance.

Some kind of ray, Roentgen decided, was coming from the Crookes tube, going through its black paper wrapping, crossing over to the bench and causing the crystals to glow, or fluoresce. Fascinated, he switched the tube back on, reached for a nearby book, held it between the tube and the cardboard and found to his astonishment that the crystals continued to glow.

Barely able to control his excitement, Roentgen closeted himself alone in the laboratory. For the next few days and nights he proceeded to test a number of other substances in place of the book. Whatever he held between the tube and the cardboard—whether wood, glass, ebony, hard rubber, fluorspar—the mysterious rays kept coming through. It was the same with most metals he tried; only lead and platinum obstructed the process. He also found that photographic film was exposed when placed between the tube and cardboard.

Balm for an irate spouse

As time sped heedlessly by, Mrs. Roentgen demanded an explanation of her husband's prolonged absences from home. This wifely reaction was to have more than the usual repercussions. Roentgen brought her to the laboratory, placed a paper-wrapped sheet of photographic film under her hand, exposed it to the tube and thereby created one of history's most famous pictures. When developed, the film showed the internal bone structure of Mrs. Roentgen's hand—and incidentally, the silhouette of her heavy gold wedding ring. Unable to identify the rays emanating from his tube, Roentgen labeled them X-rays.

In the world of Victorian mores, his pictures of human bones stirred outrage; unscrupulous persons, it was feared, might well employ Roentgen's rays to look through the very clothes that people wore (New Jersey state legislators tried to meet the situation by proposing a ban on the use of X-rays in opera glasses). But in the world of science, the announcement of Roentgen's discovery created a furor of a quite different sort. Crookes tubes were soon glowing and photographs were being made in laboratories all over Europe as some of the world's great physicists set to work to explain the strange phenomenon of X-rays. And within weeks, these rays had begun to serve their still-noble function of pinpointing the broken bones in human bodies.

But 17 years went by before a young Munich professor, Max von Laue, conceived the notion that X-rays might have yet another vital and valuable use: to examine the arrangement of atoms within a solid. Von Laue reasoned that the rays might be diffracted by the crystals inside solids —producing an effect akin to that achieved by a glass prism on a beam of light. Thus, when the X-rays encountered any regular structure of atoms

STRENGTH IN SHARING
A carbon atom unites with another carbon atom by a "covalent bond," which is visualized in the drawings below where a house stands for the inner part of the atom and children are the outermost electrons. An atom of carbon has four electron-children playing in different corners of its yard *(first drawing)*. The second drawing shows that one of them has found a playmate from another carbon atom. The two households are now linked together by what chemists call a covalent bond.

A CARBON ATOM

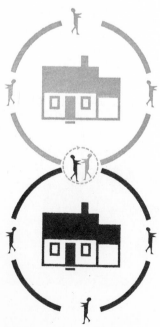

within a crystal the resulting diffractions, too, might form patterns.

Under Von Laue's direction, two of his assistants aimed a fine beam of X-rays at a crystal of copper sulphate. A photographic plate was placed some distance behind the crystal and the X-ray beam was kept running for several hours. Upon developing the plate, the experimenters found a symmetrical pattern of black blobs, each blob corresponding to a location where X-rays were diffracted within the crystal.

This experiment represented a double breakthrough. First, it showed conclusively that X-rays were like light, but of a much shorter wavelength (some scientists had thought they might be tiny particles); second, it proved that the remarkable regularity of crystal shapes was due to the harmonious arrangement of their basic atomic units.

The X-ray diffraction technique has since proved itself man's most valuable tool to date in probing into structure, whether it be the structure of crystals or the structure of genetic molecules of his own body. It has pried out of solids secrets whose implications are still but dimly appreciated, but which have already enabled man to construct alloys many times stronger and more resistant to heat than any ever known on earth; it has enabled him to create a whole repertoire of synthetics, each with properties tailor-made to its function; it has even enabled him to probe into one of the innermost secrets of life itself, the structure of the molecule that controls the heredity of mankind and all of life.

Von Laue's photographs of 1912 plainly suggested that the crystal was composed of successive planes, or layers, of atoms. Within the crystal these formed lattices—something like a tiny jungle gym or steel skyscraper structure. This finding fascinated a father-and-son team of English scientists, William Henry Bragg and his 22-year-old son William Lawrence. Experimenting on their own, the Braggs developed a mathematical formula for calculating how the regularly spaced crystalline structures should reflect X-rays, that is, how the different X-ray waves might mix with one another as they bounced up from the various layers of atoms. By the proper measurement of the spots of light and dark formed by the diffraction patterns, it was possible to determine the thickness of each of the layers inside the crystal—thus the distances between atoms.

The tenants of a latticework

From the Braggs' work emerged a whole new advance in the science of crystallography and a swiftly growing class of specialists—the solid-state physicists, so called because they concentrated on the behavior of matter in its solid rather than in its liquid or gaseous state. Gradually these men built up a picture of the solid as a crystalline latticework of atoms, with each atom in its own rigid niche in which it could not move

STRENGTH IN LOSING

A lithium atom unites with a fluorine atom by an "ionic bond," which is visualized in the drawings below. The atom of lithium gives up its one high-spirited, fidgety electron to the actively greedy fluorine household, which has three pairs of electrons plus one loner who needs a playmate. The lithium child leaves its atom completely and loses its identity. But the lithium atom, solicitous for its lost electron, remains close by to create what chemists call an ionic bond.

A LITHIUM ATOM

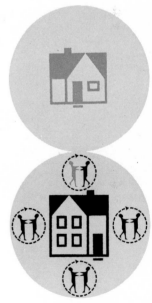

AN IONIC BOND

A LITHIUM ATOM

A METALLIC BOND

STRENGTH IN WANDERING

A lithium atom unites with another lithium atom by a "metallic bond," which is visualized in the drawings at left. An atom of lithium has one very free and restless electron—so restless that it will wander from neighbor to neighbor, never staying in its own backyard. Its neighbors' offspring are equally vagabond. All these wandering children, shared equally by the households of the neighborhood, are a source of physical strength: they create a metallic bond.

except to vibrate a bit. What ties one atom to a neighbor atom is a bonding force of electrical attraction between the total positive charge of one atom and the negatively charged electrons of the other. In all, there are four varieties of such bonding, and it is the subtle differences between them that account for the particular properties of solid substances—their solubility, their conductivity, the ease with which they melt or freeze, and so on.

In "ionic" bonding, such as exists in the crystals of common salt, or sodium chloride, an atom of sodium loses one of its electrons to an atom of chlorine, creating charged particles—ions—of such strong attraction for each other that the resulting bond is extremely tough; thus, for example, high temperatures are needed to melt crystals of table salt.

The private life of a diamond

In "covalent" bonding, one atom shares one or more electrons with another atom, a link that produces tremendous hardness. Both diamond and graphite—two forms of pure carbon that are chemically identical yet physically far different—are examples of covalent bonding. While the diamond is the hardest substance known to man, graphite is "soft" enough to be used as a lubricant. Yet, paradoxically, in some directions the bond between graphite's atoms is actually stronger than the bond between the diamond's, because within each layer of the graphite crystal the atoms are closer together. At the same time, the layers of a graphite crystal lie at such a great distance from each other that only a very weak bond exists between the atoms of different layers. This allows the layers to slip freely over one another, and accounts for the excellent lubricating quality of graphite.

Metals have a special kind of bonding, "metallic bonding," directly responsible for their conductivity of heat and electricity. In a metal crystal the atoms are closely packed together and their bonding forces are similar to covalent bonding forces, except that specific electrons are not shared between specific atoms; instead the electrons exist in a kind of roaming cloud, free to travel and hook up between any two atoms in the lattice. It is this cloud that comprises an electric current, drifting through the crystal when an electric field is applied. The same cloud also conducts heat. As heat is applied at one spot, the free electrons gain speed in random directions and, in colliding with other particles in the crystal, transfer this heat throughout the material.

The fourth type of bonding in solid crystals is provided by the same Van der Waals forces that, as noted in Chapter 4, hold the molecules of liquids together. These forces, which link molecules rather than atoms, are relatively weak. Occasionally certain of the molecules break away from their neighbors and fly off helter-skelter into space. This explains,

CHARGE OF AN ELECTRON BRIGADE
The four diagrams below show how metals conduct electric currents. When a current is absent, electrons jump randomly from atom to atom, never leaving the "neighborhood," as represented by the child bouncing from house to house. A current applied to a poor conductor, such as the coil of a toaster, is like a gang of unruly children charging into the neighborhood to liven things up at several houses before they leave at the other end. In a good conductor, such as a copper wire, the gang runs through fast, stopping at few houses. And in some substances, when the temperature is down near absolute zero (−459.7° F.), the electrons stop visiting; the metal has become a superconductor.

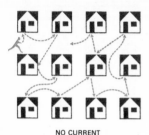

NO CURRENT

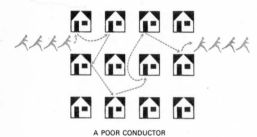

A POOR CONDUCTOR

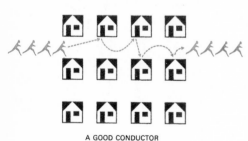

A GOOD CONDUCTOR

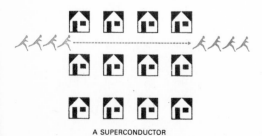

A SUPERCONDUCTOR

for instance, why iodine sublimes so readily, that is, passes directly from the solid to the gaseous state without going through the liquid state.

More than one kind of bonding may occur within a single crystal. Furthermore, although individual atoms have fixed positions within their lattice, they are not absolutely immobile; their bonds are somewhat elastic and each atom can vibrate or oscillate around its assigned place in the framework. As temperature rises, motion increases, finally straining bonds to the breaking point; the crystal then melts, and the solid becomes a liquid.

Furthermore, even the crystalline structure itself can be compelled to change by the application of pressure—a fact that has spawned a whole industry. Man can now create the hardest gems by this means, including the diamond itself. The first to lay claim to this feat was a Scotsman, J. B. Hannay, who in 1880 recorded that he had achieved the transformation by heating and fusing paraffin, bone oil and metallic lithium under extremely high pressure in heavy sealed tubes. The British Museum today exhibits a number of tiny crude diamonds of high quality donated by him. Scientists question Hannay's claim because they have never been able to duplicate his experiment. But in 1955 a four-man team at the General Electric Laboratory in Schenectady, New York subjected graphite to pressure of between 800,000 and 1,800,000 pounds per square inch and to heat between 2,200°F. and 4,400°F., added a molten metal as a catalyst (a material that launches a chemical reaction but does not participate in it) and transformed the graphite into small diamonds. Such man-made sparklers have not yet been made of gem size but are turned out as a cheaper source of industrial diamonds indispensable for certain cutting, grinding and polishing operations. General Electric researchers have even created one batch of diamonds out of peanut butter—a less obvious if more toothsome source of carbon.

A handicap of purity

Virtually limitless industrial ramifications have resulted from the scientists' increased understanding of crystal structure and properties. One notable example is the field of electronics. The shirt-pocket radio and suitcase-sized electronic computer owe their existence to a 1948 Bell Telephone Laboratories invention called the transistor, yet it now seems the crudest and simplest of present electronic devices. Most solid-state electronics, including the transistor, are based on the properties inherent in quasi-metallic substances such as germanium and silicon. In very pure form, these elements are only poor electrical conductors—so-called "semiconductors"—because their electrons are linked rather tightly by covalent bonding. But this defect can be rectified by the addition of a slight trace of an impurity—antimony, arsenic or bismuth, for

THE STRANGE DOUBLE LIFE OF CARBON

The drawings below show why carbon in one of its forms is a soft greasy lubricant, graphite, and in another of its forms is the hardest natural substance in the world, diamond.

AN ALL-DIAMOND DECK

A deck of cards *(above)* is 52 slippery planes that can be separated by a flick of the finger, the cards sent sprawling over the table. But if each is glued to the one above and below, the deck becomes resistant to pressure from any direction. As explained below, diamond behaves like the deck pasted solid, graphite like the unglued cards.

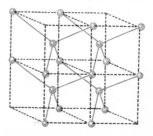

A ZIGZAG HARDNESS

The structure of diamond can be seen in the four hollow cubes above. In the center of each is a carbon atom linked by covalent bonds *(diagram, page 102)* to four other carbon atoms in different corners of the cube. The result is a complicated three-dimensional zigzagging structure that is equally hard in any direction.

A GREASY SOFTNESS

The structure of graphite can be visualized as a series of planes, like the two above, in which carbon atoms (the dots) are strongly linked in a two-dimensional hexagonal pattern. But the horizontal planes, like playing cards in a deck, are weakly held one to another. This weakness, which permits graphite to split into thin flakes, is what makes it a good lubricant.

example, whose "loose end" electrons roam about as negative electric charges, making the material mildly conductive. The addition of other impurities—boron, aluminum or gallium—which have too few electrons to link up evenly with the original atoms of the germanium and silicon leaves the structure with a "hole," or an electron deficit. This "hole" can shift around in the structure and become a carrier of positive electricity —the opposite of an electron.

Most solid-state electronics effects, such as amplification and switching of signals, are achieved when a semiconductor with one kind of impurity is placed in contact with a semiconductor with another kind of impurity. Solid-state physicists have developed minuscule crystals containing the proper mixture of impurities, which they expect will form the ultimate monolithic blocks of a new "microelectronics." Already, engineers have devised radios no bigger than a thumbnail, made up of only two or three of these blocks.

A contradiction for connoisseurs

Enormously excited over the implications of such developments, specialists in crystallography are no less exhilarated over the prospects opened up by an accidental discovery made in 1955. To gain mastery over existing crystals is one thing; to produce a crystal where none existed before is another. Among the few solid-appearing substances which are not crystalline in structure is—despite its look—glass; the fine "crystal" relished by connoisseurs is a misnomer. Glass is a form of matter difficult to classify. Like a solid, it retains a definite shape; but the molten mass of silicon compounds which go into its making solidify so quickly that their molecules do not have sufficient time to form a crystalline arrangement.

At the laboratories of the Corning Glass Works eight years ago, Dr. S. Donald Stookey was experimenting with a new type of glass—a photosensitive variety which could be etched, by photographic means, in intricate patterns. He had a batch of it in a furnace which he inadvertently left going overnight. When the overheated glass was eventually removed, it slipped from the grasp of prongs and dropped to the floor. *But instead of breaking, it bounced.* Analysis showed that it had been converted into a ceramiclike material. For the first time in history, a glass had been made with a regular crystalline molecular pattern akin to that of a metal. This fundamental new material, with a mechanical strength ranging from 15,000 to 35,000 pounds per square inch and heat-resistant to 1,300° F., now serves, among other purposes, for the making of nose cones for missiles.

The wonder products of the ever-defter manipulation of the simple crystal of a solid may seem, to the dazzled layman, almost a surfeit of

NATURE'S OWN SOLID GEOMETRY

Any crystal found on earth, whatever its size, belongs to one of the seven basic types *(below)*, whose geometrical-sounding names derive from the properties of their sides and angles. Cubic crystals have all right angles and all sides equal. The tetragonal family has all right angles and two of three sides equal. The rhombic type has all right angles but three different side lengths. Monoclinic crystals are like rhombic but "squashed" in one direction, so that eight of their angles are not right angles. Triclinic crystals are squashed in two directions; they have no right angles and three unequal sides. Trigonal is like triclinic, but with all sides equal. Hexagonal is like tetragonal, but two faces have six equal sides.

CUBIC

TETRAGONAL

RHOMBIC

MONOCLINIC   TRICLINIC   TRIGONAL

HEXAGONAL

riches. But the story of the solid does not stop with the crystal. The same penetrating insights which Wilhelm Roentgen's X-rays permitted into the heart of iron and copper have laid bare the structure of coal and wood and other organic compounds. X-ray diffraction techniques revealed that these materials were made up of groupings of giant molecules, now called "polymers"; the brilliant mimicking of this handiwork of nature has resulted, as may be seen in the picture essay on the ensuing pages, in a new world of wholly man-made solids: a stupendous parade of synthetic substances in which nylon and artificial rubber are but two of the front-line marchers.

Cellulose, the mighty structural building block of the plant and vegetable world, provides a case in point. During the 19th Century, the study of its chemical reactions with nitric acid had produced first the highly explosive nitrocellulose, or guncotton, and subsequently a sticky viscous liquid which became the base for the first man-made fiber, rayon. But not until the 1920s was the *physical* nature of cellulose understood. By X-ray analysis, two German chemists, Kurt Meyer and Herman Mark, established that cellulose consists simply of long parallel chains of sugar molecules strung together in a regular, repetitious way, 50 to 150 units long or longer, and that these chains were also characteristic of the molecules of cotton, wool, silk and all natural fibers. Rubber proved to be built quite differently: its giant isoprene molecules, while also linked in a chain, were not strung out but coiled up like a mass of tiny springs, thereby providing elasticity.

By analyzing the differences between the inherent features of cellulose, rubber and other organic substances, scientists learned that the properties of a material arise out of the structure of its molecules. The laboratory creation of a simple molecule whose properties resembled those of its natural prototype was relatively easy; the difficulty, however, lay in linking the molecules into the polymer chains which gave a particular substance its particular character.

Approach to an open-sesame

The breakthrough here—and it was to prove the open-sesame to the entire synthetic polymer industry—was achieved by a brilliant young American, Wallace Hume Carothers, in 1929, in connection with an intensive drive to find a substitute for natural rubber which could be used in event of war. Four years earlier, a research team at the Du Pont laboratories had created a close look-alike to isoprene, the natural rubber molecule; the new molecule was called chloroprene for the chlorine it contained in place of isoprene's hydrogen. But the question still remained of how to hook one chloroprene molecule to another to simulate the giant coiled chain of natural isoprene molecules. Carothers, a researcher who had come to Du Pont to head a fundamental investigation into the structure of giant molecules, had worked out a technique of so-called "polymerization."

For his monumental work of molecular welding, Carothers used as his chief tools heat, pressure and a number of catalysts. Under this massive campaign of persuasion, the separate chloroprene molecules were indeed cajoled into joining up with one another, and synthetic rubber was on its way. In a number of respects it has proved superior to natural rubber, since its chlorine atoms make it resistant to grease, weathering and sunlight.

By the 1930s chemists were building new polymers all over the lot, patiently combining and recombining basic organic materials in endless ways; nylon, for instance, could be fashioned as a fiber, to provide the softness of stockings, or it could be made compact, to provide the hardness of replacements for steel bearings. Patently, the future of synthetics is limitless, for nearly all their organic components abound in nature—not alone in coal and wood, but in oil and natural gas as well.

As man shapes nature more and more to his own design, it becomes apparent that the traditional divisions of matter into solid, liquid and gas are mere class distinctions. They are, indeed, of moment in everyday life; but they yield to the overriding importance of the basic molecule in all of them, and even more basic, the atom.

In Man-made Matter, a Whopping Jackpot

From time to time the painstaking scientific inquiry into the complexities of matter can pay off in a spectacular jackpot. This is what happened when man finally learned, after centuries, to juggle nature's basic building materials and mold matter to his own design. Late in the 19th Century a partly synthetic plastic called Celluloid was turned into billiard balls and movie film. In 1909 Bakelite, the first wholly synthetic plastic, was patented. Then, after World War II, improved techniques and an insatiable demand suddenly created a top-ranking industry now worth $12 billion which floods the U.S. with a dazzling bounty of new textures and shapes, such as the glowing nylon houses on the opposite page. Still on the increase, this output is divided into three main categories: plastics, synthetic rubber and synthetic textiles. In one or another of these forms, man-made matter has established itself permanently in every facet of our daily lives.

A SHELTERING BUBBLE
The "airhouses" looming like translucent mushrooms opposite are all-synthetic creations of nylon fabric coated with vinyl plastic—a combination four times stronger than waterproof canvas and 40 per cent lighter. When anchored by cable or sand and inflated with air by a small blower (at left of bottom bubble), these structures provide effective shelter and storage space.

THE NYLON ROPE TRICK

Magic occurs in a beaker at the junction of two layers of chemicals. The molecular setup of the liquids is such that they "polymerize" upon meeting, to form a film of nylon. This is strong enough to be pulled out of the beaker and twisted into a rope. The process goes on spontaneously until one or both liquids are used up.

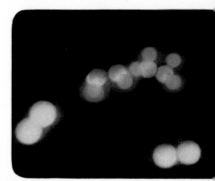

Models in a movie sequence enact the for

MAKING POLYVINYL CHLORIDE

In the structural formula at right—a kind chemical shorthand—a hydrocarbon molecu (ethylene) meets chlorine (red Cl), which d places a hydrogen atom (red H) to form vin chloride and hydrogen chloride (red HCl). T double-bonded carbon atoms (red C) then li in a giant single-bonded molecule—polymer of polyvinyl chloride, a versatile popular plast

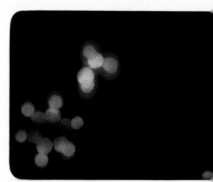

Benzene molecule, a six-sided ring of hydr

MAKING POLYSTYRENE

Here an ethylene molecule meets one of be zene, known as a benzene ring. With the loss two hydrogen atoms (blue H), styrene is forme and polymerizes to make polystyrene. The ca bon atoms (blue C) of each molecule link t gether to provide a carbon backbone for ea polymer. This process is called "addition pol merization": that is, the molecules hook toget er, usually under heat and pressure in huge a toclaves, or "kettles." The nylon-making proce at left is called "condensation polymerization that is, the joining molecules compress togeth to squeeze out another chemical, such as wate

The First Step in Making Synthetics: Molecules Meet

The work horses in the formation of all synthetics are hydrocarbon molecules. Plentifully supplied by nature in the form of coal, oil and natural gas, these alliances of carbon and hydrogen atoms come in all shapes and sizes. They have a special genius for hooking up with one another and with other types of molecules to form the giant molecules called polymers. These can join together by the thousands or the hundreds of thousands to produce an almost endless variety of chain formations. When these in turn mass together in great enough quantity, they change into a solid. This process is called polymerization. Something like it occurs in nature to produce substances like rubber and wood. In man's laboratories polymerization is the basis of all synthetic rubbers and plastics, such as the nylon in genesis at left.

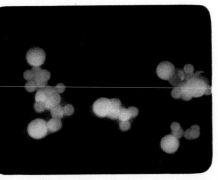 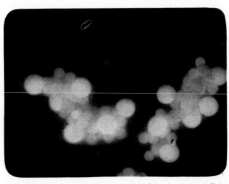 

low: yellow chlorine molecules meet ethylene molecules made of hydrogen (red) and carbon (blue) and join to form a plastic used in shower curtains.

Ethylene + chlorine *yields* vinyl chloride + hydrogen chloride. Vinyl chloride + vinyl chloride + vinyl chloride *yields* polyvinyl chloride.

 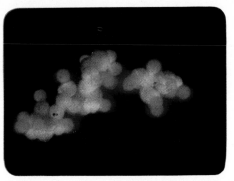 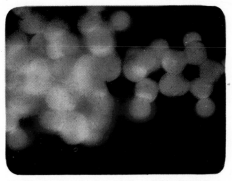

ed) and carbon (blue), meets an ethylene molecule and polymerizes to make the giant molecules of polystyrene, used in toys and kitchenwares.

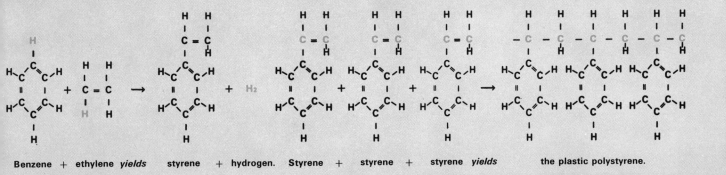

Benzene + ethylene *yields* styrene + hydrogen. Styrene + styrene + styrene *yields* the plastic polystyrene.

111

SYNTHETIC FIBERS

The fibers used in these and all other synthetic textiles are not thought of as plastics, although they are made the same way, by polymerization of simple materials. The two fabrics at left are Dacron (7), the other cloth and carpet samples are nylon (5).

COATINGS

Synthetics are widely used for protective covering. The paint base and glove coating are synthetic rubber (12) while the other items are protected by plastics from various families: (9), boots, carton and cable; (13), tool handle; (8), nonstick frying pan.

WOOD
COTTON   SULPHUR
SALT   NATURAL GAS
LIMESTONE   COAL
WATER
FLUORSPAR   OIL

1. **Acrylics:** *limestone, coal, air, water, gas, sulphur;* 2. **Cellulosics:** *wood or cotton, limestone, coal, water;* 3. **Epoxies:** *oil, air, salt, water;* 4. **Melamines:** *gas, limestone, coal, air, water;* 5. **Nylons:** *air, gas, oil, salt, water;* 6. **Phenolics:** *gas, oil, sulphur, water;* 7. **Polyesters:** *oil, salt, air, limestone;* 8. **Polyfluorocarbons:** *gas, salt, fluorspar, sulphur, water;* 9. **Polyolefins:** *oil or gas;* 10. **Polystyrenes:** *oil;* 11. **Polyurethanes:** *oil, air, gas, limestone, salt;* 12. **Synthetic Rubbers:** *oil, gas, air, salt, sulphur, water;* 13. **Vinyls:** *limestone, oil, salt, air, coal.*

A MERE SAMPLING OF TODAY'S SYNTHETIC BOUNTY

Heaped in the hopper at right are 13 of the most common families in the genealogy of synthetic polymers. They are produced through controlled polymerization from the abundant natural ingredients listed above them. Inasmuch as each family boasts several members, the proliferation of synthetics has resulted in at least 50 commercial varieties. Their names are often jawbreakers (the telephone below, for instance, is made of Cycolac acrylonitrile-butadiene-styrene) and their identities are many-sided and hard to pin down.

Some of these versatile materials appear in several guises: flexible or rigid, clear or opaque, colorless or multi-hued. They can turn up as film, foam or fiber, in all manner of products. The wide variety of these products is underscored by the examples on this chart. The synthetic rubbers, fibers and various forms of plastics are grouped separately. The numbers in parentheses have been inserted to give reference to the families listed at right.

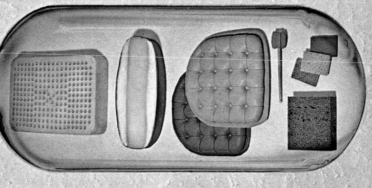

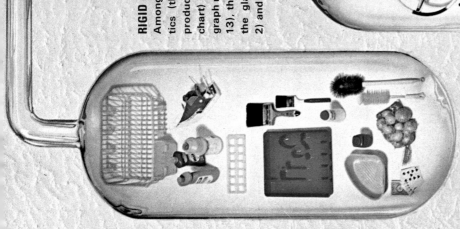

PLASTIC FILMS

Several prolific plastic families are represented here. Various vinyls (13) are used for the safety float, ball. Saran Wrap and water-soluble packages at lower right. Other wrappings are polyethylene (9); camera film and tape are cellulose acetate (2).

FOAMS

The mattress at top is a synthetic rubber foam, and the other items are plastic foams, made by allowing gas to bubble through the liquid plastic during its forming. The halved cushion and the sponges are polyurethane (11); the seat cushions are vinyl (13).

SYNTHETIC RUBBERS

These materials (12) resemble plastics in many ways but are classed separately chiefly because of their elasticity, a property not usually found in plastics. Synthetic rubber can be relatively hard (shoe sole and shopping-cart wheel) or flexible (flippers).

RIGID PLASTICS

Among the most versatile plastics (they all appear in other products elsewhere on this chart) are those in the phonograph record (polyvinyl chloride, 13), the juicer (polyethylene, 9), the glasses (cellulose acetate, 2) and the rifle stock (nylon, 5).

FLEXIBLE PLASTICS

The housewares, bottles and toy are made of polyethylene (9), the commonest and one of the lightest plastics. The washable playing cards are cellulose acetate (2), which in a rigid form goes into combs. The net bag at the bottom is polyethylene (9).

A late shift lights up a Chemstrand nylon plant.

The Growing Appetite of a Young Colossus

As a major industry, synthetic polymer production and processing is less than two decades old, but by now there are nearly 8,000 U.S. firms involved in it. Every year this booming giant develops new materials, methods and machines for spinning, extruding and molding its growing list of new commodities. And hosts of new uses are found for old products.

Basic to this burgeoning business is the complicated preparation of the hundreds of different chemicals used in polymerization. These are combined to form the raw synthetic material, generally in the form of a syrupy liquid, powder or pea-sized pellets. In plastics-processing plants this raw stuff is treated with heat, and is pushed, pulled, squeezed and ballooned into innumerable shapes. Most plastics are compressed, blown or injected directly into molds to form a range of finished products from automobile bodies to salad bowls. Other plastics are extruded into continuous sheeting, tubes or film (opposite). Tiny synthetic fibers are spun into yarn for weaving into cloth (below). Tires and other resilient items are molded from synthetic rubber—which now accounts for three quarters of all U.S. rubber consumption. All told, a staggering 12 billion pounds of raw synthetics a year are fed to the industry's insatiable machines.

TWO-WAY STRETCH FOR A SLEEVE

A nearly transparent film of polyethylene is extruded at the Du Pont Company *(right)*, a major producer of this plastic. Air blown into the sleeve as it leaves the machine stretches the film horizontally at the same time it is pulled vertically. This gives its long molecules a two-way orientation for greater strength. Extruded film is wound on reels and slit for use, primarily in packaging. Film is also produced by squeezing plastics between rollers.

HIGH-SPEED RIDE FOR YARNS

In one of the final steps before weaving begins, shining synthetic yarns whiz through a slashing bath in a J. P. Stevens Company textile plant. Slashing is a chemical treatment which keeps the fibers from fraying and breaking. Because of their strength and fast-drying properties, synthetic fibers have become a potent factor in the textile business. But to offset their nonabsorbent quality they are often combined with natural fibers in clothing fabrics.

A Host of Uses and the Promise of More to Come

The huge difference in the size and function of the objects on these pages—the tiny artificial valves for the heart (*below*) and the 13-story balloon for outer space (*right*)—offers a good measure of the extraordinary range of synthetics in their innumerable roles. They have proved a source of materials for the most exacting and often offbeat jobs. For instance, the sweeping machines that try to keep New York City clean wore out brushes every 115 miles until they were equipped with nylon bristles. Now a brush will scrub 2,600 miles of dirty street. One of the most versatile plastics is fluorocarbon, which is so tough it can be made into protective suits capable of withstanding flashes of 3,000°F. heat. At the same time it is so slippery it can make lubrication-free bearings for automobiles and airplanes.

Synthetics are also fully enrolled in space exploration. Rocket nose cones are often plastic, and all the best-dressed astronauts have worn working suits of synthetic rubber and aluminized nylon. From the space race to boat racing is an easy transition for synthetics: about one million yards of man-made fiber fabrics are made into sails annually, and close to 50 million pounds of plastics go into the construction of boats. Less sporty but more vital are plastics' contributions to communications, from television to telephones to Telstar. There seems to be no doubt that when the first man lands on the moon, synthetics will land with him.

A PLACE IN THE HEART
The odd shapes on the table above are bits and pieces of plastic fashioned in pioneering efforts to make a substitute human heart. While that exciting possibility has not yet been realized, other artificial organs are already being used in a whole new medical discipline based on synthetic materials. Plastic arteries, sutures and "bone glue" are also being used in surgery.

AT HOME IN OUTER SPACE
Dwarfing men and machines in a dirigible hangar in Weeksville, North Carolina, is Echo II, a passive communications satellite. Here being tested by National Aeronautics and Space Administration engineers, the 135-foot inflatable sphere is made of a .00052-inch-thick sandwich of two pieces of aluminum and plastic film. It weighs 500 pounds and folds into a 40-inch container.

6

Mapping the Terrain of the Atom

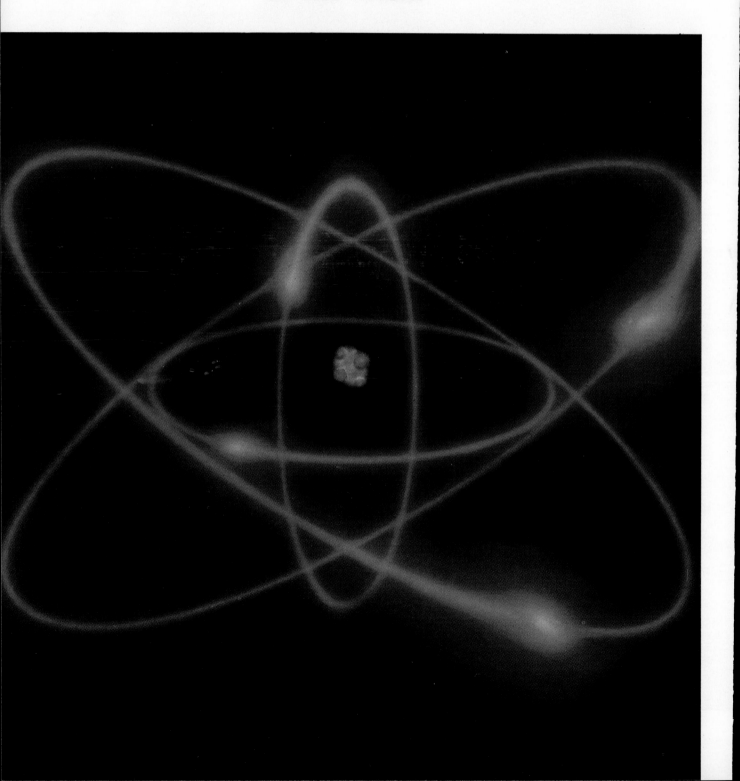

THERE must be few places in the world where people are unacquainted with the whirling, airy symbol that we use to depict the atom—a glowing nucleus shaped like a bunch of grapes, enmeshed within the intertwined loops of orbiting electrons. It is the very trademark of our age. Yet what reality lies behind the symbol? Did the atom ever sit for its portrait?

The truth is that no one has ever seen an atom, for it is far too small to see. Even if magnifying lenses could be made powerful enough, light waves themselves are so coarse that the atom would still defy visual examination; it would be like trying to feel the texture and angles of a grain of sand with hands encased in boxing gloves.

Nevertheless, bit by bit, the minute terrain of the atom has been mapped—from evidence that, taken piece by piece, is the most circumstantial imaginable. Taken as a whole, however, this evidence has built up a picture of the atom with proven usefulness, as demonstrated by the nuclear weapon and the power reactor. The accumulation of hints has been one of the most massive, protracted and diligent detective jobs ever undertaken by science.

Man began speculating about atoms long before science became an organized activity. Even to the ancient Greeks it appeared sensible to assume that there might be some kind of ultimate building blocks of matter. Then, many centuries later, the great Isaac Newton concluded that matter was formed in ". . . solid, massy, hard, impenetrable, moveable particles . . ."—in other words, that the atom was something like a billiard ball. Newton's idea was pure speculation. The first man to reason the atom's existence by cold intellectual deduction from a fact in nature was John Dalton, early in the 19th Century. As noted in Chapter 2, Dalton developed a theory of the relative atomic weights of elements. In so doing, he became fascinated by the fact that when elements combine together to form new compounds, they always combine in proportions that can be expressed neatly in whole numbers. Such numbers occur so rarely in physical nature that they are considered a signal flag of hidden meaning. Dalton arrived at the conclusion we now know to be correct: every element must be composed of fundamental units—"ultimate particles," characteristic of that element and no other.

This explanation of matter was enough to satisfy the chemists. They felt no need to probe much further, since chemical reactions operated only on the atom's outer fringes. As it turned out, the atom was breached by that plaything of the physicists—electricity. By the century's end, they were tidying up their mathematical descriptions of electrical phenomena and looking for new fields to conquer. In the course of exploring the fascinating properties of electricity, the physicists had built up a highly successful experimental technique and had devised some remarkably sensitive apparatus.

AN ATOM IN REPLICA
The model of an enlarged beryllium atom in the photograph opposite shows how subatomic particles are spatially related. The atom's four electrons *(blue)* whirl around a nucleus composed of five neutrons *(green)* and four protons *(red)*. To make this model entirely accurate in its proportions would necessitate placing the innermost electrons 25 yards from the nucleus.

One particular piece of laboratory gadgetry opened up a whole new line of inquiry into the atom. This was the cathode-ray tube, generally called the Crookes tube after the ingenious English scientist William Crookes. It was simply a glass tube with wires sealed into both ends—a cathode, or negative terminal, and an anode, or positive terminal. When air was drawn out of the tube and the wires were connected to a source of high-voltage electricity, a fluorescent glow appeared on the glass wall of the tube. Crookes had shown that this was caused by a ray emitted by the cathode. All that was known about these cathode rays at the time was that they traveled in straight lines. But the phenomenon created an enormous stir. Exploring the properties of a Crookes tube led Wilhelm Roentgen to his discovery of X-rays in 1895, as recounted in Chapter 5. This momentous accident in turn led to another, which quickened scientific curiosity about the atom all the more.

Saga of a sunless day

In France, Henri Becquerel happened to be working with potassium uranyl sulphate—a compound of the fateful element uranium—to see if it would generate X-rays when struck by sunlight. By chance one day, when the sun was not out, Becquerel put the compound atop a wrapped photographic plate and set it aside in a drawer. Later, almost as an afterthought, he developed the plate and found to his great surprise that it had a black image on it, a rough silhouette of the piece of uranium salt. Something in the compound—some form of radiated energy—must have penetrated the wrapping of the plate and exposed it the way light does. Coming only two months after the discovery of X-rays, this potent energy apparently issuing from the heart of a solid material posed new puzzles. Where did the energy come from? Out of the cold uranium itself?

Becquerel suggested to his good friends, Pierre Curie and his Polish-born wife Marie, that they investigate the mystery further. They began looking into the properties of uranium ore, called pitchblende, and quickly discovered that in addition to uranium there was at least one other substance in the ore that emitted radiation—and far more intensely than uranium itself. They set about isolating this substance. After two years of arduous labors in a miserable shed, the Curies finally were able to reveal to the world not one but two brand-new elements that gave off these strange energies. One of these, as everyone knows, was radium; the other was named polonium, after Mme. Curie's native country.

Meanwhile, the intellectual fallout from Roentgen's X-ray discovery had drifted across the English Channel. At Cambridge University's Cavendish Laboratory it set off a burst of productive activity that made the laboratory world-famous. There two men who were to become the principal explorers of the atom's interior settled down to experiment with

FALLOUT'S POTENT PROGENY

In early experiments with uranium ores, scientists like Henri Becquerel and Marie Curie discovered three main types of radiation with different powers of penetration. These are the same emanations produced by atomic bomb fallout, and their danger to human life is proportional to their power to pierce shielding. The diagram at right shows radiation from a sample of an unstable element such as polonium. The alpha particles emitted from the sample are the weakest radiation, for they cannot penetrate an ordinary sheet of paper. Beta particles, or electrons, are more energetic, but can be blocked by an inch-thick layer of wood. The most penetrating are gamma rays, a powerful sort of X-ray which requires a thick layer of concrete as protective shielding.

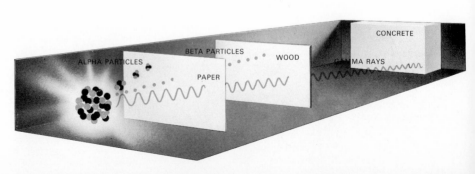

the effects of X-rays on gases. The older of these men was the director of Cavendish, Joseph John Thomson, known as "J.J." The younger was a brilliant, 24-year-old New Zealander named Ernest Rutherford, who had just arrived in England on a research fellowship and had been hired as Thomson's assistant. A hulking, hearty man, Rutherford loved the world of experimental gadgetry and his flashes of insight from what the gadgets told him were phenomenal.

Working as a team, Thomson and Rutherford studied what happened to a gas when it became a conductor of electricity under the influence of X-rays. Thomson speculated that this conductivity resulted from some sort of unseen positively and negatively charged particles generated in the gas by the X-rays, a phenomenon called ionization. He theorized that they might even be part of the legendary atom itself—a heretical thought in view of the still widely accepted concept of the atom as an indivisible billiard ball.

Thomson turned his attention to the negatively charged particles, for he suspected that it was a volley of these particles that made up the cathode rays shooting through a Crookes tube. Experiments performed by others before him had shown that Crookes tube rays can be bent by bringing a magnet near the tube. Thomson, using electric as well as magnetic fields, measured the amount of bending and thus was able to determine the ratio of the electric charge each particle carried to its mass. He also determined the particle's velocity. The technique he employed was analogous to determining the weight of a steel bullet by firing it near a magnet of known strength and seeing how much the bullet's flight is diverted from the target's bull's-eye. In 1923, the American physicist Robert A. Millikan won a Nobel Prize for measuring the *actual* charge of this particle, thereby permitting its mass to be determined with great accuracy. Calculations eventually established that the negative particle weighed 1/1,840 as much as a whole hydrogen atom.

A singular raisin cake

The particle that Thomson had discovered became known as the *electron*, which he then went on to fit into a new picture of the atom. He visualized a sphere of some kind of positive electricity throughout which his tiny negative electrons were loosely embedded like raisins in a cake. Every element had a different number of electrons in its atoms, and these electrons were always arranged in a particular, regular way.

Thomson gave Rutherford the job of learning everything he could about the nature of both positive and negative particles—how rapidly they were formed, how long they lasted, how swiftly they would move to their opposite positive or negative electrical pole. In time Rutherford and others discovered that uranium and other substances emitted at least

OBSERVER OF A MINUSCULE WORLD
Though he produced artificial diamonds and discovered the element thallium, Sir William Crookes is best known for his experiments with electron beams, conducted in primitive vacuum tubes akin to the one shown in this famous *Vanity Fair* caricature. Crookes's researches provided techniques which were to be used in determining atomic structure.

three different kinds of rays. When, for example, radioactive material was put into a lead container, the rays emanating from a hole in the container could be separated into three branching streams by bringing a powerful magnet near. One would be bent slightly in one direction, a second would be bent more sharply in the opposite direction, and the third would not be bent at all.

The first of these streams was attracted to a negative electric terminal and was not very penetrating; most of it was stopped by a single sheet of paper or a few inches of air. Rutherford himself named this stream alpha rays. The second stream, which he called beta rays, was attracted to a positive electric pole and was quite a bit more penetrating than the alpha rays. Moreover, it resembled in several other ways the fast-moving stream of particles in a Crookes tube—the very particles Thomson had identified as electrons. The final set of rays, the unbendable ones, were the most penetrating of all, and, in fact, closely resembled X-rays. These were labeled gamma rays by their discoverer, Paul Villard.

In 1898 Rutherford left Cavendish Laboratory to take a professorship at McGill University in Canada—a more lucrative post that enabled him to marry the girl he had left back home in New Zealand. At McGill he and coworkers turned out a brilliant series of papers proving that the atoms of radium transmute themselves into the atoms of other elements in a series of radioactive disintegrations. Furthermore, he showed that the alpha ray must be a massive charged particle, probably the positive ions of helium gas. It was this alpha particle that he chose for his subsequent probe into the heart of the atom.

Preface to a deft device

In 1907 Rutherford returned to England to become professor of physics at the University of Manchester. He took on as a helper Hans Geiger, an aspiring physicist from Germany whose name has become one of the household words of the atomic age. Together, Rutherford and Geiger developed or adapted several devices for counting individual alpha particles—in effect ancestors of the Geiger counter. One was the scintillation counter, basically a disk coated with zinc sulphide. The impact of an alpha particle on the screen produces a tiny flash of light, or scintillation, visible through a microscope.

When a young Manchester undergraduate named Ernest Marsden joined them as a laboratory assistant, Rutherford asked Geiger to guide him through an experiment to build up his experience. Though devised as a routine exercise, it was to have profound consequences. The experiment involved seeing what would happen if alpha particles were fired at a metal foil. Rutherford was fairly sure that the particles would go right on through the foil with very little deviation in their paths.

THOMSON'S ATOM (1898)
MINUS CHARGES IN A POSITIVE SPHERE

LENARD'S ATOM (1903)
PAIRS OF PLUS AND MINUS CHARGES

NAGAOKA'S ATOM (1904)
ELECTRONS ORBITING A POSITIVE COR

After all, if Thomson's electron-studded model was correct, the atom had no particles or concentration of forces within it big enough to deflect the heavy alpha particle drastically.

Geiger and Marsden set up a radioactive alpha particle source, a metal foil target and, off to the side, a zinc sulphide detector screen, which was shielded from the source—but not the target—by a lead block. They then focused a microscope on the detector screen. As their eyes became accustomed to the dark, they saw a number of scintillations on the screen, announcing the arrival of alpha particles. Since the screen was blocked off from the radioactive source, these particles could only have come from the foil target—and if so, they had literally bounced off the target. The two neophyte scientists blurted their finding to "Papa," as their boss was called, and left him equally astonished. As Rutherford put it later, "It was about as credible as if you had fired a 15-inch shell at a piece of tissue paper and it came back and hit you."

The mystery of a bounce

Rutherford went to the heart of the question: how could a fast-moving particle that weighed thousands of times as much as an electron bounce off a group of atoms that (according to Thomson's description) were little more than fuzzy balls studded with electrons? The only conclusion Rutherford could draw was that an electrical force was responsible for deviating the relatively massive particles from their forward path—an immensely powerful force that must be concentrated in a tiny volume, since only a few particles were drastically diverted. Most of the particles would miss this area entirely or only brush close by it, and an exceeding few would hit it head on.

From this supposition, Rutherford went on to draw an entirely new picture of the atom. It was an incredibly tenuous atom, whose bulk was mostly empty space. It had a tiny but extremely dense and heavy central core, or "nucleus," with an outer mantle of electrons in rapid rotation about the nucleus, as the planets circle the sun. The nucleus, with its powerful positive electric charge, was the seat of the force that had deflected the alpha particles in the Geiger-Marsden experiment.

After two years of further study, Rutherford, in February 1911, produced a paper entitled "On the Scattering of Alpha and Beta Particles by Matter and the Structure of the Atom." Now ranked as one of the great landmarks of scientific investigation, it hardly made a ripple in the scientific community of the day. To the world outside Rutherford's laboratory, the atom was still a billiard ball or a raisin cake.

One physicist who was, however, interested in Rutherford's atom was a young Dane, Niels Bohr, who was to become one of the giants of nuclear physics, a personal link between Rutherford's early pioneering and the

INSIDE STORY OF THE ATOM

Man's belief in the atom as a solid, indivisible particle remained unchallenged from 400 B.C. until almost 1900 A.D. But once the concept was questioned, it took only 15 years for scientists to postulate a modern atom. In the five cartoons at left that illustrate this cycle, negatively charged particles are shown in blue, with positive charges in gray.

● The first man to diagram the atom's inner workings was the Englishman J. J. Thomson. In 1898 he contended that a large number of negatively charged electrons (which he called corpuscles) were contained in a ball-shaped positive field.

● In 1903, Philipp Lenard, a Heidelberg University physicist, proposed an atomic model made up of "dynamids"—pairs of negative and positive charges floating in space.

● The next year, Hantaro Nagaoka of Japan published a surprisingly modern description: to him, the atom was a circlet of electrons around a heavy center. He compared the atom to the ringed planet Saturn, which remains stable because the core is massive enough to attract and hold its rings in their proper orbits.

● By 1911, New Zealander Ernest Rutherford concluded that the atom's positive charge was concentrated at its center, with electrons swarming around this nucleus.

● Two years later, the Danish physicist Niels Bohr modified this idea with his theory that all electrons move within distinct spherical shells. In his hydrogen atom, shown immediately at left, the one electron moves around the nucleus in a specific circular orbit.

RUTHERFORD'S ATOM (1911)
ELECTRONS ENCOMPASSING A NUCLEUS

BOHR'S HYDROGEN ATOM (1913)
AN ELECTRON CIRCLING A NUCLEUS

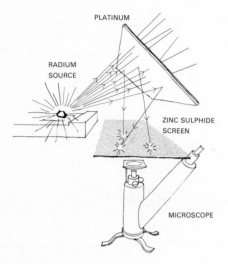

MIRROR ON THE ATOM

The device shown here provided physicists Hans Geiger and Ernest Marsden with data that later proved the atomic nucleus was an extremely dense structure. A thin platinum foil was placed near a small quantity of radium, a good source of alpha particles; to the great surprise of the experimenters, one in each 8,000 particles bounced back from the platinum, producing a tiny flash on the nearby zinc sulphide detector screen which could be observed through a microscope. Geiger and Marsden concluded that only the presence of small, dense nuclei in the platinum atoms could produce such a strong reflection.

atomic bomb itself. Bohr plunged into a certain theoretical problem concerning the electrons in Rutherford's solar-systemlike atom—a problem Rutherford himself was aware of. It was all very well to imagine that the electrons were held in neat orbits by their rapid whirling around a powerfully attracting central "core" but, according to the classical laws of physics, an electrical charge under such conditions would radiate light, or other energy, for much the same reason that X-rays were produced from Roentgen's Crookes tube. Furthermore, it would radiate away all its energy, and quickly spiral into the nucleus.

Bohr took a high-handed way out of this predicament: he flatly asserted that the electron would *not* dissipate its energy. In support of this assumption he found useful a new theoretical speculation—later to be developed into the quantum theory—that had been propounded by a German, Max Planck, in 1900. Behind Planck's quantum equations was a revolutionary concept: that radiation (light or any form of radiant energy) was never emitted as a continuous stream but rather in small, discrete packets called "quanta" (from the Latin *quantus*, or how much).

Energy on a staircase

Applying this notion, Bohr blandly assumed that, contrary to what classical physics taught, an electron *could* circle its nucleus forever without radiating away its energy, but it was not permitted to whirl about in just any circle. Bohr clamped down on the electron's freedom, restricting it to certain orbits. While in any given orbit, the electron had a specific energy. It could jump to another orbit, but it had to do it in one leap. And only in the process of changing orbits did it give off or absorb energy. It was as though each electron rested on a staircase; to climb one step it had to be given a packet of energy, and when it fell down one step it yielded a packet of energy. In a Crookes tube filled with hydrogen gas, for example, energy is fed into each hydrogen atom in the form of high-voltage electricity, raising its single electron into a higher orbit. After a while, the electron can fall back to its lower orbit; when it does so, it may emit a quantum of energy, which shows up as a beautiful red in the spectrum—hydrogen's characteristic color.

At first, Bohr worked out his theory of electron behavior on hydrogen, which he assumed to have only one electron in its atom. When other scientists went on to develop a more general picture of all the elements, they were presented with something of a puzzler. How were they to know for certain how many electrons were in the atoms of the various elements? Perhaps the answer lay in Mendeleyev's Periodic Chart, which gave each element an atomic number, ranging from 1 for hydrogen to 92 for uranium. As we saw in Chapter 2, the real significance of these atomic numbers was hidden when Mendeleyev compiled the table.

THE ATOMIC SHELL GAME

The classic portrait of the atom is a dense nucleus of protons and neutrons (dark blue), surrounded by electrons (black dots) which orbit within spherical shells. As the size and charge of the nuclei increase, electrons are pulled closer, and the shells become smaller. Thus the diameter of the innermost shell of carbon, with its nucleus consisting of six protons and six neutrons *(far right),* is only one quarter that of one-proton hydrogen.

HYDROGEN—
ONE ELECTRON
IN A SHELL

HELIUM—
TWO ELECTRONS
IN ONE SHELL

In 1913, before he went off to die in World War I, the brilliant 26-year-old British physicist Henry Moseley demonstrated that the number of electrons in each element's atoms was identical to its atomic number. Twelve years later, the Austrian-born Wolfgang Pauli mapped in the number of electrons that occupied each of the atom's concentric shells, accounting for the way chemical properties derive from the number of electrons in the all-important outer shell.

The map of the atom sketched in from Rutherford's original theory gradually won wider acceptance from the scientific community. A minute entity, only two billionths of an inch in diameter, it is a complex architectural system containing as many as a hundred electrons racing in ceaseless circles around an incredibly small nucleus. If a hydrogen atom's nucleus were enlarged to the size of a golf ball, its single electron would be describing its orbit about a mile away. Yet this electron zips around so fast that it makes over a hundred million billion circuits every second. It is this everywhere-at-once character of the electron in orbit that makes for the solidity and rigidity of the atom's structure.

But, however neat and satisfactory, Bohr's picture of the atom is not the end of the story. Bohr's atom was based on a view of matter as consisting of discrete particles. Actually, there is just as much evidence that all matter has wave properties.

Since Newton's day there has been a simmering controversy as to whether a light beam is composed of separate tiny particles, or of waves. For some time physicists were convinced that light consists of waves because they found that the different colors of light must correspond to different frequencies of such waves, and that they could interact to produce "beats," just as sound waves of slightly different frequencies do in the air. But in 1905, Albert Einstein, through his 17-page, Nobel Prize-winning paper on the "photoelectric effect," was able to explain why light appeared to hit a target and knock loose electrons in exactly the sporadic manner that separate particles would—not in the smooth, continuous way that one would expect from waves. In sum, Einstein was saying that light consisted of particles.

The ruminations of a prince

In the same year this introspective, soft-spoken young man of 26 went on to revolutionize physics in wider fields with his Theory of Relativity, which, among other things, equated matter with energy. Many of the brilliant minds of this brilliant era in science fell under Einstein's spell. One was Prince Louis de Broglie, a scion of a noble French family. Accepting at face value the possibility that light might simultaneously be composed of particles and yet be wavelike, De Broglie went on, in 1923, to reason that perhaps all matter was similarly constituted. If light were

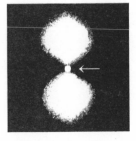

A CLOUD OF UNCERTAINTY
Rather than think of an electron's orbit as a specific circular path, scientists usually refer to a "probability cloud," within which an electron is likely to be found.
If a hydrogen atom is at room temperature, this cloud is spherical, but at higher energy levels—near an electric spark, for example—hydrogen's electron would be found within a dumbbell-shaped cloud around its nucleus (white dot), as shown above.

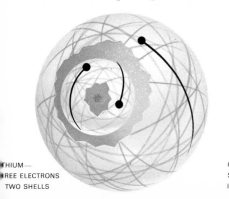

LITHIUM—
THREE ELECTRONS
TWO SHELLS

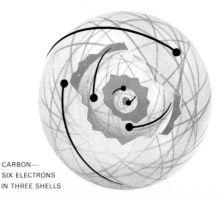

CARBON—
SIX ELECTRONS
IN THREE SHELLS

125

energy and electrons were matter and if, according to Einstein, the two were varieties of the same thing, it might well be that they would have other qualities in common as well. No one knew how such a thing could be, nor even how one could visualize such a wave-particle electron, but these were heady times.

Soon the Viennese physicist Erwin Schrödinger, looking over Einstein's and De Broglie's speculations, came forth with an all-encompassing mathematical equation that could serve as the foundation for any such wave phenomena. This was in 1926. Only a year later, De Broglie's abstract speculation that electrons were wave particles was to become quite a bit more than speculation. Two Americans, C. J. Davisson and L. H. Germer, working at the Bell Telephone Laboratories, found that electrons were diffracted from a crystal surface in the same way that X-rays had been—and in the same way that light was diffracted from a diffraction grating.

These were but a few of the complex and paradoxical advances in this fateful time for physics. As will be seen in the next chapter, a strange mathematical technique called quantum, or wave, mechanics, altered the picture of the atom still further.

The Earthy
and Elegant Community
of Elements

The vast welter of physical objects in the world around us springs from a relative handful of elements. How many originally existed in the earth's endowment is unknown, for some radioactive elements may have long since decayed away; others are disappearing. Offsetting this shrinking bounty, man is mass-producing artificial elements and finding uses for natural elements once neglected. Man-made plutonium, first turned out by the microgram during World War II, now is stockpiled in tons. Germanium, of little interest a decade ago, is now the core of the transistor industry. The 103 elements known today sit for family-group portraits on the following pages. Each family is pictured against the same tinted background as in the periodic table opposite; each element, photographed in color, is examined with regard to its particular place within the hierarchy of matter.

MATTER'S WELL-SET TABLE
The periodic table opposite lists all 103 known elements. Horizontal rows are called families or groups and are numbered in Roman numerals from I to VIII with smaller divisions labeled as A and B. Vertical columns list the elements in order of their increasing weight. Hydrogen, which has unique properties, is listed alone. Above the letter symbol for each element is the atomic number, equal to the number of protons in the nucleus.

Below is the atomic weight, the weight of one atom compared with the weight of a carbon atom established as exactly 12. Where the number is in parentheses, the element is unstable and has several different forms (isotopes). The figures to the left of the symbols represent the numbers of electrons from inner to outer orbit. The line stairstepping from boron to astatine separates the metals above from the nonmetals below.

A TABLE OF THE ELEMENTS

Left-hand family labels: Alkali and Alkaline Earth Metals · First Transition Metals · The Triads (Second Transition Metals) · Third Transition Metals · Boron and Carbon Families · Nitrogen and Oxygen Families · The Halogens · Inert Gases · Hydrogen

Hydrogen

Electron config	Number	Symbol	Atomic weight
1	1	H	1.0080

Group I A (Alkali)

Electron config	Number	Symbol	Atomic weight
2,1	3	Li	6.939
2,8,1	11	Na	22.990
2,8,8,1	19	K	39.102
2,8,18,8,1	37	Rb	85.47
2,8,18,8,1	55	Cs	132.91
2,8,18,32,18,8,1	87	Fr	(223)

Group II A (Alkaline Earth)

Electron config	Number	Symbol	Atomic weight
2,2	4	Be	9.0122
2,8,2	12	Mg	24.312
2,8,8,2	20	Ca	40.08
2,8,18,8,2	38	Sr	87.62
2,8,18,18,8,2	56	Ba	137.34
2,8,18,32,18,8,2	88	Ra	(226)

Group III B

Electron config	Number	Symbol	Atomic weight
2,8,9,2	21	Sc	44.956
2,8,18,9,2	39	Y	88.905
	57–71	Rare Earth Metals	
	89–103	Actinide Metals	

Group IV B

Electron config	Number	Symbol	Atomic weight
2,8,10,2	22	Ti	47.90
2,8,18,10,2	40	Zr	91.22
2,8,18,32,10,2	72	Hf	178.49

Group V B

Electron config	Number	Symbol	Atomic weight
2,8,11,2	23	V	50.942
2,8,18,12,1	41	Nb	92.906
2,8,18,32,11,2	73	Ta	180.95

Group VI B

Electron config	Number	Symbol	Atomic weight
2,8,13,1	24	Cr	51.996
2,8,18,13,1	42	Mo	95.94
2,8,18,32,12,2	74	W	183.85

Group VII B

Electron config	Number	Symbol	Atomic weight
2,8,13,2	25	Mn	54.938
2,8,18,13,2	43	Tc	(99)
2,8,18,32,13,2	75	Re	186.2

Group VIII B

Electron config	Number	Symbol	Atomic weight
2,8,14,2	26	Fe	55.847
2,8,18,15	44	Ru	101.07
2,8,18,32,14,2	76	Os	190.2
2,8,15,2	27	Co	58.933
2,8,18,16,1	45	Rh	102.91
2,8,18,32,15,2	77	Ir	192.2
2,8,16,2	28	Ni	58.71
2,8,18,18	46	Pd	106.4
2,8,18,32,17,1	78	Pt	195.09

Group I B

Electron config	Number	Symbol	Atomic weight
2,8,18,1	29	Cu	63.54
2,8,18,18,1	47	Ag	107.87
2,8,18,32,18,1	79	Au	196.97

Group II B

Electron config	Number	Symbol	Atomic weight
2,8,18,2	30	Zn	65.37
2,8,18,18,2	48	Cd	112.40
2,8,18,32,18,2	80	Hg	200.59

Group III A

Electron config	Number	Symbol	Atomic weight
2,3	5	B	10.811
2,8,3	13	Al	26.982
2,8,18,3	31	Ga	69.72
2,8,18,18,3	49	In	114.82
2,8,18,32,18,3	81	Tl	204.37

Group IV A

Electron config	Number	Symbol	Atomic weight
2,4	6	C	12.011
2,8,4	14	Si	28.086
2,8,18,4	32	Ge	72.59
2,8,18,18,4	50	Sn	118.69
2,8,18,32,18,4	82	Pb	207.19

Group V A

Electron config	Number	Symbol	Atomic weight
2,5	7	N	14.007
2,8,5	15	P	30.974
2,8,18,5	33	As	74.922
2,8,18,18,5	51	Sb	121.75
2,8,18,32,18,5	83	Bi	208.98

Group VI A

Electron config	Number	Symbol	Atomic weight
2,6	8	O	15.999
2,8,6	16	S	32.064
2,8,18,6	34	Se	78.96
2,8,18,18,6	52	Te	127.60
2,8,18,32,18,6	84	Po	(210)

Group VII A (The Halogens)

Electron config	Number	Symbol	Atomic weight
2,7	9	F	18.998
2,8,7	17	Cl	35.453
2,8,18,7	35	Br	79.909
2,8,18,18,7	53	I	126.90
2,8,18,32,18,7	85	At	(210)

Group VIII A (Inert Gases)

Electron config	Number	Symbol	Atomic weight
2	2	He	4.0026
2,8	10	Ne	20.183
2,8,8	18	Ar	39.948
2,8,18,8	36	Kr	83.80
2,8,18,18,8	54	Xe	131.30
2,8,18,32,18,8	86	Rn	(222)

Rare Earth Metals (Lanthanides)

Electron config	Number	Symbol	Atomic weight
2,8,18,18,9,2	57	La	138.91
2,8,18,19,9,2	58	Ce	140.12
2,8,18,21,8,2	59	Pr	140.91
2,8,18,22,8,2	60	Nd	144.24
2,8,18,23,8,2	61	Pm	(147)
2,8,18,24,8,2	62	Sm	150.35
2,8,18,25,8,2	63	Eu	151.96
2,8,18,25,9,2	64	Gd	157.25
2,8,18,26,9,2	65	Tb	158.92
2,8,18,28,8,2	66	Dy	162.50
2,8,18,29,8,2	67	Ho	164.93
2,8,18,30,8,2	68	Er	167.26
2,8,18,31,8,2	69	Tm	168.93
2,8,18,32,8,2	70	Yb	173.04
2,8,18,32,9,2	71	Lu	174.97

Actinide Metals

Electron config	Number	Symbol	Atomic weight
2,8,18,32,18,9,2	89	Ac	(227)
2,8,18,32,18,10,2	90	Th	232.04
2,8,18,32,20,9,2	91	Pa	(231)
2,8,18,32,21,9,2	92	U	238.03
2,8,18,32,22,9,2	93	Np	(237)
2,8,18,32,24,8,2	94	Pu	(242)
2,8,18,32,25,8,2	95	Am	(243)
2,8,18,32,25,9,2	96	Cm	(247)
2,8,18,32,27,8,2	97	Bk	(247)
2,8,18,32,28,8,2	98	Cf	(249)
2,8,18,32,29,8,2	99	Es	(254)
2,8,18,32,30,8,2	100	Fm	(253)
2,8,18,32,31,8,2	101	Md	(256)
2,8,18,32,32,8,2	102	No	(254)
2,8,18,32,32,9,2	103	Lw	(257)

THE ALKALI METALS

Soft Elements with Some Violent Tendencies

Since prehistoric times metals have been prized and worked by man. Yet familiar as are most of these hard, shiny, heavy elements, there are six silver-white metals— lithium, sodium, potassium, rubidium, cesium and francium—which most people would not recognize as metal. Indeed francium has never even been seen.

These half-dozen soft, light elements melt at low temperatures, cause burns if touched, disintegrate in air and are never found free in nature, but are always combined with other elements. The six are called alkali elements because of their explosive reaction with water to form an "alkali," or base (the opposite of an acid).

Unusual as these properties are by contrast with, for example, copper or iron, these elements are metals. The reason lies in the personalities of the metal and nonmetal atoms. Most metals have only a few —usually one or two—electrons in their outer orbits, in contrast with nonmetals, which generally have four to seven. More important, the metal atom is generally much larger than the atom of the nonmetal; that is, the distance from the nucleus to the outer electron shell is greater. Thus the few electrons that whirl in the farthest-out shell of the metal atom are only weakly attracted—and thus easily lost— by the faraway nucleus, while the close-by nonmetal nucleus holds its brood tightly.

Among the alkali metals, with very large atoms, the lone electron is so far from the nucleus that it flies off to combine with other elements at the least pretext—thus accounting for the family's violent nature.

LITHIUM, from *lithos,* meaning stone; discovered 1817; the lightest of the solid elements. Pictured here immersed in an inert oil, lithium forms a black oxide *(above)* when exposed to air. It is used in ceramics, alloys, in the H-bomb—and in treating both gout victims and manic-depressives.

2 1	3 **Li** 6.939

SODIUM, from soda; symbol Na, from its Latin name *natrium;* discovered 1807; sixth most abundant element. Metallic sodium is too violent for most everyday uses and is generally stored in kerosene as above. But its useful compounds include table salt, baking soda, borax and lye.

2 8 1	11 **Na** 22.990

POTASSIUM, from potash, an impure form of potassium carbonate known to the ancients; symbol K from its Latin name *kalium;* discovered 1807. Seventh most abundant element in the earth's crust. Its radioactivity, though mild, may be one natural cause of genetic mutation in man.

2 8 8 1	19 **K** 39.102

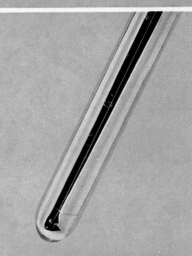

RUBIDIUM, from *rubidus,* or red (the color its salts impart to flames); discovered 1861. Rubidium, used in electric-eye cells, is also a potential space fuel. Like potassium, it is slightly radioactive, and has been used to locate brain tumors, as it collects in tumors but not in normal tissue.

2 8 18 8 1	37 **Rb** 85.47

MAKING SALT FROM THE SEA

At Hambantota, on the southeast coast of Ceylon, native workers use their bare hands to scrape up common salt, a benign compound formed by the explosive union of corrosive sodium and the poisonous gas chlorine *(pages 142-143).* The salt here was produced by letting sea water evaporate from shallow seaside ponds called salterns. A staggering 50 million billion tons of salt—containing 20 million billion tons of sodium—are dissolved in all our oceans.

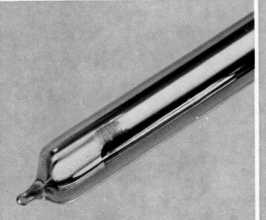

CESIUM, from *caesius,* or skyblue (its salts turn flames blue); discovered 1860; the softest metal, liquid at warm room temperature, 83° F. Extremely reactive, it finds limited use in vacuum tubes and in atomic clocks so accurate that they vary no more than five seconds in 10 generations.

2 8 18 18 8 1	55 **Cs** 132.91

FRANCIUM, for France; discovered 1939. A short-lived product of the decay of actinium, francium has never actually been seen. The graph above, which identifies francium by its radiation, is from the notebook of the discoverer, Marguerite Perey, a onetime assistant to Marie Curie.

2 8 18 32 18 8 1	87 **Fr** (223)

| 2 2 | 4 **Be** 9.0122 | **BERYLLIUM,** from the mineral beryl, in which it was found in 1798. This element produces alloys that are extremely elastic, hence its role in making gears, springs and other machine parts. Because of its high melting point—2,345° F.—beryllium goes into making rocket nose cones. |

| 2 8 2 | 12 **Mg** 24.312 | **MAGNESIUM,** from Magnesia, an ancient city in Asia Minor; discovered 1775; eighth most abundant element; burns as a powder or foil in firecrackers, bombs and flash bulbs. It has one odd biological effect: a deficiency in man can have the same effect as alcoholism—delirium tremens. |

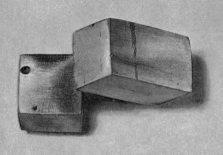

| 2 8 8 2 | 20 **Ca** 40.08 | **CALCIUM,** from *calx,* or lime —an oxide of calcium; discovered 1808; fifth most abundant in the earth's crust. Its presence in our bodies is essential. Normal quota in an adult is about two pounds, mostly in the teeth and bones. Calcium also plays a role in regulating the heartbeat. |

| 2 8 18 8 2 | 38 **Sr** 87.62 | **STRONTIUM,** from Strontian, Scotland; discovered 1790; a rare metal which is a sort of evil alter ego of life-supporting calcium. Radioactive strontium 90 is present in atomic fallout. It is absorbed by bone tissue in place of calcium, and enough of it destroys marrow and can cause cancer. |

| 2 8 18 18 8 2 | 56 **Ba** 137.34 | **BARIUM,** from *barys,* heavy or dense; discovered 1808; to minimize oxidation, the sample above was photographed in argon. The white sulphate is drunk as a medical cocktail to outline the stomach and intestines for X-ray examination. Barium nitrate gives fireworks a green color. |

| 2 8 18 32 18 8 2 | 88 **Ra** (226) | **RADIUM,** from *radius,* or ray; discovered 1898 by Pierre and Marie Curie; sixth rarest of the elements. Shown above is radium bromide mixed with zinc sulphide—a mixture used in luminous watch dials. The radium gives off dangerous radiation which causes the zinc sulphide to glow. |

A CALCIUM CENOTAPH
The marble Washington Monument attests to the structural role of calcium, whose compounds, besides forming marble, serve as the "steel-girders of life"—in the skeletons or shells of most animals

A Down-To-Earth Family and Its Jet-Set Neighbors

The alkaline earths are the quieter cousins of the blustering alkali metals. So named because they were first isolated from their earthy oxides, alkaline earths are also found compounded in many common rocks such as limestone and basalt. The reason for their relative stability is in their atomic structure. The radius of the atoms is smaller than that of the alkali metals, and their two outer electrons which make for chemical reactivity are more tightly held.

Of the six elements in the family, magnesium is perhaps best known. With only half the weight of aluminum, it forms featherweight aluminum-magnesium alloys widely employed in aircraft. Beryllium is an important alloying metal and while it is not particularly hard itself it lends a hardness to many other elements.

This hardening quality is carried over into the group of transition metals pictured below and on the following two pages. Chromium, vanadium and tungsten give a supertoughness to steel.

This first "transition group" starts the transition from metals to nonmetals. Its members tend to be hard and brittle, with high melting points. The transitional character of these elements stems from a peculiarity of their electronic structure. In the case of "typical" elements, the number of electrons in the outer orbit goes up as the atomic number goes up. With transition metals, a rise in atomic number also indicates an increase in electrons—but not in the outer orbit. All of the transition metals keep at most two electrons in their outer orbit while their next-inner orbit "fills up" with electrons.

21 Sc 44.956

SCANDIUM, from Scandinavia; discovered 1879. Although no practical uses have yet been found for this metal, its potential is great because it is almost s light as aluminum and has a much higher elting point. A pound of scandium produced 1960 was the first such quantity made.

39 Y 88.905

YTTRIUM, from the town of Ytterby, Sweden, where it was discovered in 1794; a scaly metal with an iron-gray sheen. Yttrium 90, a radioactive isotope, has a dramatic medical use in needles which have replaced the surgeon's knife in killing pain-transmitting nerves in the spinal cord.

22 Ti 47.90

TITANIUM, from Titans, the supermen of Greek myth; discovered 1791. Although it is the ninth most abundant element, titanium has only begun to serve man: its white dioxide goes into bright paints. The metal itself will be used in constructing the supersonic aircraft of the 1970s.

40 Zr 91.22

ZIRCONIUM, from zircon, the name of the semiprecious gem stone in which it was discovered in 1789. A metal unaffected by neutrons, zirconium rves as the inner lining of reactors in nuclear bmarines and atomic power plants. It is also ed as a building material for jets and rockets.

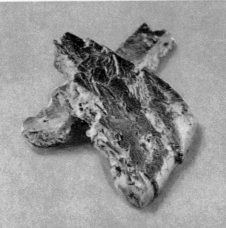

72 Hf 178.49

HAFNIUM, from Hafnia, the Latin name for Copenhagen; discovered 1923. A "wonder metal" of the atomic age, hafnium has a great appetite for neutrons. Thus it goes into neutron-absorbing reactor control rods which slow down nuclear chain reactions and also quench atomic "fires."

23 V 50.942

VANADIUM, from Vanadis, a Scandinavian goddess; discovered 1830. Added to steel, vanadium produces one of the toughest alloys for armor plate, axles, piston rods and crankshafts. Less than one per cent of vanadium and as little chromium make steel shock- and vibration-resistant.

131

2 8 18 12 1	**41** **Nb** 92.906

NIOBIUM, from Niobe, daughter of the mythical Greek king Tantalus (niobium is found with tantalum); discovered 1801. Used in steel, atomic reactors, jet engines and rockets, it was known until 1950 as columbium, from Columbia—a poetic name for America, where its ore was first discovered.

2 8 18 32 11 2	**73** **Ta** 180.95

TANTALUM, from King Tantalus of Greek myth; discovered 1802. Almost impervious to corrosion, tantalum is vital in surgical repairs of the human body: it can replace bone (for example in skull plates); as foil or wire it connects torn nerves; as woven gauze it binds up abdominal muscles.

Atlas missiles in production at an astronautics plant in California are fitted with dime-thick skins

2 8 13 1	**24** **Cr** 51.996

CHROMIUM, from *chroma*, or color; discovered 1797. A very bright, silvery metal, it forms compounds valued as pigments for their vivid green, yellow, red and orange colors. The ruby takes its color from chromium. Besides lustrous chrome plate, its alloys include a number of special hard steels.

2 8 18 13 1	**42** **Mo** 95.94

MOLYBDENUM, from *molybdos*, or lead—first found in what was thought to be lead ore; discovered 1778. Fifth highest melting metal, it is used in boiler plate, rifle barrels and filaments. No vessel could be found in which to cast it until a special water-cooled crucible was devised in 1959.

2 8 18 32 12 2	**74** **W** 183.85

TUNGSTEN, from Swedish *tung sten*, or heavy stone; symbol W from its German name *wolfram*; discovered 1783. The highest melting of metals— 6,170° F.—tungsten in filaments withstands intense heat in light bulbs. New tungsten-tipped "painless" dental drills spin at ultrahigh speed

Id-rolled stainless steel which because of its content of chromium and nickel, possesses a tensile strength of up to 200,000 pounds per square inch.

25
Mn
54.938

MANGANESE, from *magnes*, or magnet—its ore was first confused with magnetic iron ore; discovered 1774. Manganese, which gives steel a hard yet pliant quality, seems to play a similar role in animal bone: without it, bones grow spongier nd break more easily. It activates many enzymes.

2
8
18
13
2
43
Tc
(99)

TECHNETIUM, from *technetos*, or artificial; produced 1937. The first man-made element, it was originally produced by the atomic bombardment of molybdenum. Later it was found among the fission products of uranium. The six-gram sample above, no bigger than a marble, is worth $540.

2
8
18
32
13
2
75
Re
186.2

RHENIUM, from the Rhine provinces of Germany; discovered 1925. Rhenium is the ninth scarcest element and has the second highest melting point. It is used in "thermocouples" (electric thermometers for measuring high temperatures) and in the contact points of electrical switches.

At the famed "ships' graveyard" on New York's Hudson River, rusting hulls show the reaction of iron with oxygen: rust is iron oxide.

SECOND TRANSITION METALS

Three Families of Elements That Are Good Mixers

The nine lustrous, gray-white transition metals shown on the opposite page are known as the triads because they are grouped in threes. The first triad—iron, cobalt and nickel—are all strongly magnetic. They mingle easily and an alloy of all three plus aluminum and copper produces a metal called alnico which is used in making a small powerful magnet 12 times as powerful as the same-sized steel counterpart.

The next two triads, called the light and heavy platinums, are also effective mixers. Alloys among the six of them—and there are dozens of different recipes—find wide use in jewelry and in precision instruments.

Iron, nickel and cobalt all occur in pure form in nature and, oddly enough, they all occur together. But in this state they are from another world. The lumps in which they exist, sometimes many tons in weight, are meteorites. Early man probably used this metal for tools before he learned to smelt iron from its ores.

Both platinum and palladium occur as pure nuggets which are part of the earth's own endowment. But these metals are so little eroded by time and wear that a major source is old platinum and palladium objects melted down and reused.

Among the familiar elements, few are closer in their electronic structures than are iron, cobalt and nickel: each of them has two electrons in its outer orbit, with 14, 15 and 16 electrons respectively in the next-inner shell. The two platinum triads are related almost as intimately.

134

26
Fe
55.847

IRON, from *iren,* its Old English name; symbol Fe from its Latin name, *ferrum;* first utilized by prehistoric man. The fourth most abundant element and e cheapest metal, iron is the basic ingredient all steel. Making up part of the compound he- oglobin, it carries oxygen in the blood stream.

2 8 15 2
27
Co
58.933

COBALT, from *kobold,* or evil spirit (its poisonous ores were once treacherous to mine); discovered 1735. For centu- ries cobalt's blue salts have given color to porcelains, tiles and enamels. Its alloys go into making jet propulsion engines, and a radioactive isotope is used to treat cancer.

2 8 16 2
28
Ni
58.71

NICKEL, from the German *kupfernickel,* or false copper, a reddish ore containing nick- el but no copper; discovered 1751. Its hard, durable quali- ties have long made nickel popular for coins— our own five-cent piece is 25 per cent nickel, the rest copper. Nickel plate protects softer metals.

44
Ru
101.07

RUTHENIUM, from *Ruthenia,* Latin for Russia; discovered 1844. Pure ruthenium is too hard and brittle to machine. It makes a top-notch "hardener," owever, when it is alloyed with platinum. But sed in excess of 15 per cent, ruthenium is ruin- us, making the metals too hard to be worked.

2 8 18 16 1
45
Rh
102.91

RHODIUM, from *rhodon,* or rose (its salts give a rosy so- lution); discovered 1803. Be- sides forming alloys, rhodium makes a lustrous, hard coating for other metals in such items as table silver and camera parts. A thin film of vaporized rhodi- um deposited on glass makes excellent mirrors.

2 8 18 18
46
Pd
106.4

PALLADIUM, after the aster- oid Pallas; discovered 1803. Free from tarnish and corrosion- resistant, palladium is incorpo- rated in contacts for telephone relays and high-grade surgical instruments. It is also used with gold, silver and other metals as a "stiffener" in dental inlays and bridgework.

76
Os
190.2

OSMIUM, from *osme,* or odor; discovered 1804. A met- al with a pungent smell, it is used to produce alloys of ex- treme hardness. Pen tips and lifetime" phonograph needles are 60 per cent smium. It is the densest metal known: a brick- ized chunk of osmium weighs about 56 pounds.

2 8 18 32 15 2
77
Ir
192.2

IRIDIUM, from *iris,* or rain- bow, so named for its colorful salts; discovered 1804. Very hard and hence extremely dif- ficult to work or cast, iridium hardens other metals. Its alloys make bars used as standard weights and measures. The inter- national "standard meter" is platinum-iridium.

2 8 18 32 17 1
78
Pt
195.09

PLATINUM, from *platina,* or little silver; discovered 16th Century. Found in nuggets of up to 21 pounds, it is used not only in weights and measures but also in jewelry, delicate instruments and electrical equipment. Once as costly as $175 an ounce, its value has dropped to a mere $80.

Two Clans:
One Moneyed,
One Mundane

Three transition metals—copper, silver and gold—are almost opposite in their properties to the alkali metals. Rather than being light, soft and reactive, these metals are rather heavy, hard and inert. Whereas the alkali metals are never found free in nature, these transition elements often occur in pure nuggets. Yet both groups of metals have a single electron in the outer orbit of their atoms—and thus ought to show similar chemical properties.

The key to their differences lies in their next-to-last electron orbit. Most alkali metals have eight electrons in that shell. And eight is a magic number in electron circles. It is the most stable possible arrangement the outermost orbit of an atom can have. Hence the alkali metals react violently to get rid of their pesky outer electron to achieve a kind of atomic nirvana. But copper, gold and silver have not eight but 18 electrons in their second last shell. Even if they lose their outer electron they are still far from the stability of eight. Thus they are discouraged from reaction, which accounts for their appearance in nature in pure form.

While an alluring aura has always surrounded gold, silver and copper because of their use in money and jewelry, the second family shown here—zinc, cadmium and mercury—is more prosaic. Cadmium alloys are common in high-speed bearings of automobile, aircraft and marine engines. Zinc is ubiquitous in the household "galvanized," or zinc-coated, pail. Mercury, familiar in thermometers, is the one liquid metal, solidifying only at −38°F.

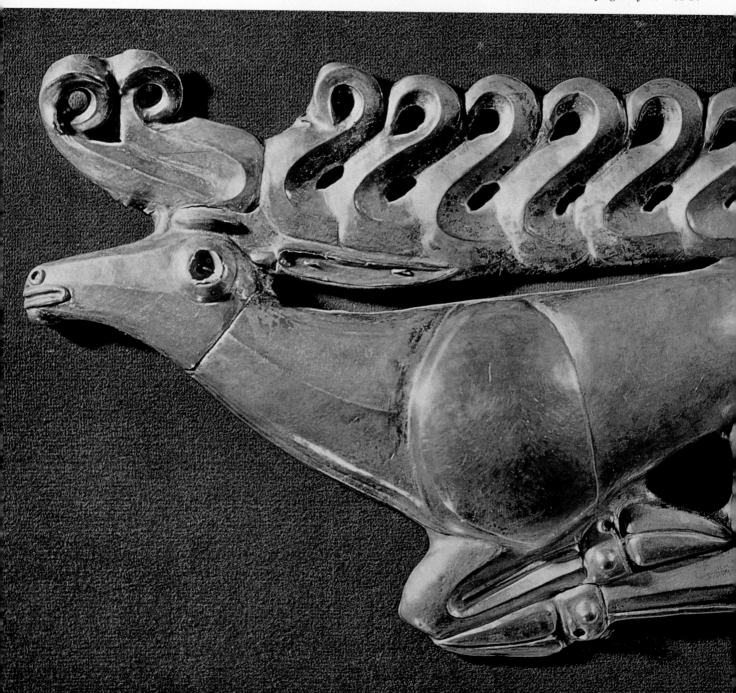

his Fifth Century gold stag, once affixed to a
arrior's iron shield, was an adornment of no-
ads who fought on the steppes of Central
sia during the seven centuries before Christ.
old is the 16th rarest of the elements; the
otal world production from 1493 to date—
orth about $70,875,000,000—could all be
elted down into a 50-foot cube. Fortunately,
he metal is durable; gold in use today undoubt-
dly was part of some Egyptian treasure horde.

COPPER, from *cuprum*, derived from the ancient name
for Cyprus, famed for its copper
mines; known by early man. It
and gold are the only two col-
ored metals. Alloyed in most gold jewelry and
silverware, copper is mixed with zinc in brass,
with tin in bronze. A "copper" penny is bronze.

2 8 18 1 — 29 **Cu** 63.54

ZINC, probably from *zin*, German for tin; discovered by the
alchemist Paracelsus in the
16th Century, though the zinc-
copper alloy brass was known
to the ancients. While not technically a colored
metal, zinc has a bluish cast. An excellent coating metal, it is used to line flashlight batteries.

2 8 18 2 — 30 **Zn** 65.37

SILVER, from Old English *seol-
for*, for silver; symbol Ag from
its Latin name *argentum*; prehistoric; the best conductor of
heat and electricity. Its salts
are basic in photography: when silver bromide
is exposed to light, it undergoes a chemical
change which the developer then makes visible.

2 8 18 18 1 — 47 **Ag** 107.87

CADMIUM, from *kadmia*, or
earth; discovered 1817. Cadmium occurs in nature with
zinc. It makes excellent neutron-eating rods to slow up
atomic chain reactions and finds use in nickel-
cadmium batteries. Its bright sulphide makes
the artist's popular pigment, cadmium yellow.

2 8 18 18 2 — 48 **Cd** 112.40

GOLD, from the old English
word *geolo*, or yellow; symbol
Au from its Latin name *aurum*;
prehistoric; the most malleable
metal. Man's lust for gold has
been a delusion, for he has pursued little more
than a yellow gleam. It cannot be used for
much besides money, jewelry and dental work.

2 8 18 32 18 1 — 79 **Au** 196.97

MERCURY, from the planet
Mercury; symbol Hg from *hydrargyrum*, or liquid silver; prehistoric. It appears in the glass
tubing of thermometers and
barometers; it also finds use in "silver" dental
inlays and in silent electric switches. Vaporized
mercury fills modern blue-hued street lights.

2 8 18 32 18 2 — 80 **Hg** 200.59

137

BORON, from borax and carbon; discovered 1808. A nonmetal, boron is best known in borax (sodium borate) and in boric acid—the one acid that is good for the eyes. About a million tons of boron are used in industry each year. In agriculture it serves as both a plant food and weed killer.

2	3
5	
B	
10.811	

ALUMINUM, from *alumen,* or alum; discovered 1827. The most abundant metal and third most abundant element, its uses range from toothpaste tubes to airplane wings. Early samples cost $545 a pound; now over a million tons are produced yearly in the U.S. for as low as 15 cents a pound.

2	8	3
13		
Al		
26.982		

GALLIUM, from *Gallia,* the o name for France; discovere 1875. A metal that melts in th hand, it is also the only one th expands as it freezes, as do no metals and most gases. Its high boiling poi (3,601° F.) makes it ideal for recording tem peratures that would vaporize a thermomete

2	8	18	3
31			
Ga			
69.72			

INDIUM, from the indigo blue it shows in a spectroscope; discovered 1863. A metal used in engine bearings, in transistors and as a "glue" that adheres to glass, it is too scarce for large-scale use. But miniscule, long-lived indium battery has been devised to power new electronic wrist watches.

49 **In** 114.82

THALLIUM, from *thallos*, or a young shoot—its spectrum is a bright-green line; discovered in 1861. Its chief use is in thallium sulphate—a deadly rat poison. Odorless and tasteless, it is mixed with starch, sugar, glycerin and water to make an inviting if ominous "treat" for household rodents.

81 **Tl** 204.37

CARBON, from *carbo*, or charcoal; prehistoric. Shown above in its natural forms—diamond, charcoal and graphite—carbon in its endless variety of compounds is an indispensable source of such varied everyday products as nylon and gasoline, perfume and plastics, shoe polish, DDT and TNT.

6 **C** 12.011

THE BORON AND CARBON FAMILIES

The Thin Line between the Metals and Nonmetals

The boron and carbon families are a motley crew: black, brown, white, soft, hard, metallic and nonmetallic. No other group of elements is so varied. Presumably this is because they are near the halfway point in the periodic table; with three or four electrons in their outer shell, they lie squarely between alkali super metals and super nonmetal halogens *(pages 142-143)*.

Out of this no man's land comes man himself and indeed all of life. It is because carbon acts somewhat like a metal and somewhat like a nonmetal that it can combine in a fantastic variety of ways. There are well over two million carbon compounds (called organic compounds), about one and a half times the number formed by all the other elements combined (inorganic compounds). Somewhere among this vast array of carbon substances, still unidentified, lie the living molecules which have proliferated to produce all life forms. Scientists searching for some other element which might also serve as a basis for life find only one—silicon, carbon's closest kin—and they think life on other planets may be based upon this glassy element.

BEAUTY OUT OF BLACKNESS

Diamonds, a girl's most glittering friend, are basically no different from the graphite in a pencil—both are carbon. They vary only in the way their atoms are arranged in crystals. The bauble on the brow opposite, the world-famed "Idol's Eye" unearthed about 1600, has fetched as high as $675,000 in the course of its checkered career.

SILICON, from *silex*, or flint; discovered 1823; the second most abundant element—making up one fourth of the earth's crust. Sand, largely silicon dioxide, goes into making glass and cement. Pure silicon is used in micro-electronic devices such as solar batteries to power satellite instruments.

14 **Si** 28.086

GERMANIUM, named for Germany; discovered 1886. The first metal in the carbon family, germanium resembles the nonmetal silicon. The first element used for transistors, it has brought about the replacement of large vacuum tubes with devices one four-hundredth of an inch across.

32 **Ge** 72.59

TIN, an Old English word; the symbol Sn from *stannum*, Latin for tin; prehistoric. Because it does not rust and resists other corrosion, tin has made possible the housewife's delight, canned food. A tin can is steel, coated with about 0.0005 of an inch of tin. Over 40 billion such cans are made each year.

50 **Sn** 118.69

LEAD, from Old English *lead;* symbol Pb from its Latin name, *plumbum,* also the origin of plumber; prehistoric. Enormously durable, lead has been the backbone of plumbing for centuries. The lead pipes once used to drain the baths of ancient Rome have been uncovered still in working order.

82 **Pb** 207.19

2 5	7 **N** 14.007

NITROGEN, from *nitron* and gen, or niter-forming; discovered 1772; a gas making up 78 per cent of the air. Nitrogen is extremely inert, yet its compounds include the anesthetic "laughing gas," explosives such as TNT, fertilizers, and amino acids—the building blocks of protein.

2 8 5	15 **P** 30.974

PHOSPHORUS, from *phosphoros*, or light-bearer; discovered 1669; occurs in three major forms—white, red (both above) and, rarely, black. The white, so unstable that it yellows, then reddens in light, glows in the dark—hence "phosphorescence." Phosphates are ingredients of detergents.

2 8 18 5	33 **As** 74.922

ARSENIC, from *arsenikos*, or male (the Greeks believed metals differed in sex); discovered about 1250. Best classed as a nonmetal with a few metallic traits, arsenic is famed as a poison but some of its compounds are medicines. When heated, it "sublimes"—i.e., the solid vaporizes directly.

2 8 18 18 5	51 **Sb** 121.75

ANTIMONY, from *antimonos*, "opposed to solitude" (it generally occurs mixed with other elements); symbol Sb from *stibium*, or mark (it was once used as eyebrow pencil); discovered about 1450. Antimony is mixed with lead in batteries and goes into type metal and pewter alloys.

2 8 18 32 5	83 **Bi** 208.98

BISMUTH, from the German *wissmuth,* or white mass; described 1450. The most metallic member of its family, bismuth melts at 520° F. but forms alloys that melt at as low as 117° F. These find wide application in electric fuses, solders and in automatic fire-sprinkler systems.

2 6	8 **O** 15.999

OXYGEN, from *oxys* and gen, or acid-forming; discovered 1774; the most abundant element, making up about half of everything on earth, 21 per cent of the atmosphere by volume and two thirds of the human body. Breathed in by animals, oxygen is restored to the air by plants.

2 8 6	16 **S** 32.064

SULPHUR, from *sulphur*, brimstone—its Biblical name recognized since ancient time. Used in all branches of modern industry, it turns up, among other places, in matches, insecticides and rubber tires. Nearly 200 pounds of sulphuric acid per capita are produced in the U.S. each year.

140

NITROGEN AND OXYGEN FAMILIES

Two Groups with Many-faceted Personalities

Except for nitrogen, the gaseous and solid elements in the two families on these pages share one characteristic: each exists in more than one form in nature. These several forms—called allotropic—vary as to texture, color and chemical behavior, depending either on the number of atoms in a molecule of the gas, or on the way the atoms are arranged in the solid. The most familiar example is oxygen, O_2, which also exists as ozone, O_3.

The five nitrogen family elements all have five electrons in their outer orbit. Yet from the lightest (nitrogen) to the heaviest (bismuth) their properties shift from nonmetallic to metallic. In heavier members the outermost electrons are farther from the nucleus and thus more easily lost; the "freer" the outer electron, the more metallic is the atom. The five oxygen family elements all have six electrons in their outer orbit. From the lightest (oxygen) to the heaviest (polonium) they similarly tend to metallic behavior.

NITROGEN'S COLOSSAL MIGHT

At Seymour Narrows, British Columbia, in 1958 the explosive potential of nitrogen was released to end a shipping peril—an underwater mountaintop. In history's biggest nonnuclear blast, 1,375 tons of nitrates were detonated, moving some 690,000 tons of rock and sea water.

SELENIUM, from *selene*, or moon; discovered 1817; exists both as metal and nonmetal. Unlike most electrical conductors, selenium varies in conductivity with variations in light. This "photoelectric" trait suits it for service in electric eyes, solar cells, television cameras and light meters.

2 8 18 6
34
Se
78.96

TELLURIUM, from *tellus*, the earth; discovered 1782. With both metallic and nonmetallic traits, tellurium has several peculiarities. It is "out of step" in the periodic table, having a lower atomic number but higher atomic weight than iodine. And inhaling its vapor results in garlicky breath.

2 8 18 18 6
52
Te
127.60

POLONIUM, after Poland; found in 1898 by Pierre and Marie Curie in pitchblende. The scarcest natural element, it was the first to be discovered by the Curies. It is shown here as a thin film on a stainless-steel disk, the form in which it is sold as an alpha-particle source for scientific use.

2 8 18 32 18 6
84
Po
(210)

HYDROGEN AND THE HALOGENS

A Lone Wolf and a Family of Aggressors

Hydrogen is unique among the elements: no one family can claim it. Its nucleus consists of one proton, around which spins a single electron. It is sometimes grouped with the alkali metals (which also have one outer electron), but there is as much reason to place it with the halogens: like hydrogen, each of the halogens precedes an inert gas in the periodic table. An active gas, it is "diatomic"—i.e., hydrogen molecules consist of two atoms clinging together. At great heats, the nuclei of two atoms "fuse," releasing vast amounts of energy (as in the H-bomb).

The group of elements known as the halogens are in their own way as active as hydrogen. All have seven electrons in their outer orbit: thus they readily "pick up" an electron from other atoms to form electrically charged "ions." The name halogen, in fact, comes from the Greek word *hals*, salt, and the suffix gen, "producing" or "forming," inaccurately adapted from the Greek "to be born." These elements are distinctly nonmetallic: their outermost electrons are so tightly held that they are rarely lost in reactions with atoms of other elements. The halogens are found in all three familiar physical states. Fluorine and chlorine are gases; bromine is the only element besides mercury that is a liquid at room temperature; iodine and astatine are solids. Halogens are poisonous, corrosive and are potent antibacterial agents. Tincture of iodine is a good antiseptic; sodium fluoride added to water in a process called fluoridation reduces tooth decay caused by bacteria.

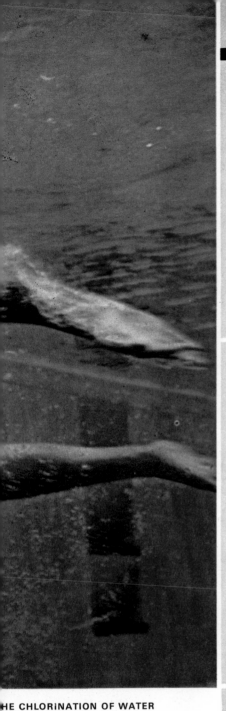

HYDROGEN, from *hydor* and gen, or water-forming; discovered 1766; third most abundant and lightest element. Hydrogen is almost never found free on earth, but the sun and other stars are almost pure hydrogen. The thermonuclear fusion of hydrogen nuclei lights and heats the universe.

1
H
1.0080

FLUORINE, from *fluo*, or flow; discovered 1771. Fluorine is the most reactive of the nonmetals; only a few of the inert gases resist it. It corrodes platinum, a material that withstands most other chemicals. In a stream of fluorine gas, wood and rubber burst into flame—and even asbestos glows.

2
7
9
F
18.998

CHLORINE, from *chloros*, or greenish-yellow; discovered 1774. Combining with almost as many elements as fluorine, chlorine is less corrosive but strong enough to be used as a bleach, a disinfectant and a poison gas. Pure chlorine is commonly prepared from ordinary salt (NaCl).

2
8
7
17
Cl
35.453

BROMINE, from *bromos*, or stench; discovered 1826; a red, caustic, fuming liquid with a foul smell. Bromine is an effective disinfectant. Among its compounds are the bromides, used in nerve sedatives and in gasoline antiknock compounds that make automobile engines run smoothly.

2
8
18
7
35
Br
79.909

THE CHLORINATION OF WATER
Performing a hard "tumble turn," an Australian swimmer practices in an indoor pool. Swimming pools are disinfected, as are most large-scale public water supplies, by the addition of one part of chlorine to every million parts of water. The chlorine does not itself kill off bacteria; this is done by the atoms of "free" oxygen of H_2O released by the chemical reaction of chlorine with water. Although oxygen is needed to support life, too much of it is lethal.

IODINE, from *ioeides*, or violet; discovered 1811; a blue-black solid which turns into a violet vapor when heated. Formerly prepared from seaweed, it is now produced from oil-well brines. Most table salt is now "iodized" to supplement the human diet; an iodine deficiency causes thyroid trouble.

2
8
18
18
7
53
I
126.90

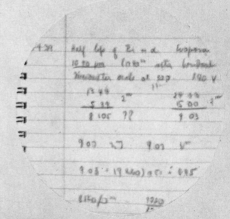

ASTATINE, from *astatos*, or unstable; discovered 1940. Astatine, prepared by bombarding bismuth atoms with helium nuclei, is radioactive and has a maximum half life of 8.3 hours. Its detection is recorded (*above*) in the notebook of one of its discoverers, American physicist D. R. Corson.

2
8
18
32
18
7
85
At
(210)

A Staid Clan That Lives According to Its Lights

The gases known variously as inert, noble or rare form almost no compounds with other elements. And indeed the atoms of the same inert gas will not couple; all other gases exist in molecules of two atoms, for example O_2, H_2 and Cl_2. These unreactive elements are among the rarest known; neon, krypton and xenon are the seventh, fifth and fourth scarcest of the natural elements. While helium can be extracted from natural gas and radon is obtained as a product of radium's decay, the only source of the other inert gases is the air. Comprising less than 1 per cent of the atmosphere, they are produced commercially by the delicate fractionation of liquid air. Each of the gases boils off at a slightly different temperature and is collected in pure form.

The unsociable nature and extreme stability of inert gases is due to their electronic structure. Because the outer orbit of each is completely filled with electrons, these atoms have almost no incentive either to lose or gain electrons in the presence of other atoms. Only recently, in one of the major—and most startling—achievements of modern chemistry, several of these sluggish elements have been coaxed to combine with the gas fluorine.

All of the inert gases on these pages, except radon, were sealed into glass tubes and photographed as an electric charge passed through the tube, causing the gases to glow with their distinctive colors. Radioactive radon was placed on a background of zinc sulphide, thus causing it to glow with a yellow-green light.

THE RADIANCE OF RARE VAPORS
The multicolored lighting which gives Tokyo its famed night glow *(opposite)* is produced by a mixture of neon and its related gases. At top, a sign advertises a sewing machine as a woman stitches colored designs on "neon cloth." The lower sign touts milk chocolates and caramels.

HELIUM, from *helios,* or sun; discovered in 1868. Almost all the helium in the world comes from natural gas wells in the United States. One well in Arizona produces a gas that is 8 per cent helium. Lighter than air, it is widely used in blimps and balloons in place of highly flammable hydrogen.

2 / **He** / 2 / 4.0026

NEON, from *neos,* or new; discovered 1898. The best known of the inert gases, it is chiefly used in advertising. The ubiquitous "neon sign" is a glass vacuum tube containing a minute amount of neon gas: when an electric current is passed through, the tube gives off a bright orange-red light.

2 8 / **Ne** / 10 / 20.183

ARGON, from *argon,* or inactive; discovered 1894. The most abundant of noble gases, argon makes up 0.934 per cent of the air. Its industrial forte is in welding: it provides an inert atmosphere in which welded metals will not burn. It is also the gas that fills ordinary incandescent light bulbs.

2 8 8 / **Ar** / 18 / 39.948

KRYPTON, from *kryptos,* or hidden; discovered in 1898. Radioactive krypton is used to keep tabs on Soviet nuclear production. Because this gas is a by-product of all nuclear reactors, the Russian share is found by subtracting the amount that comes from Western reactors from the total in the air.

2 8 18 8 / **Kr** / 36 / 83.80

XENON, from *xenos,* or stranger; discovered 1898. The rarest gas in the atmosphere, xenon is used in specialized light sources such as the high-speed electronic flash bulbs used by photographers. In these, the high volatility of its electron structure produces an instant, intense light.

2 8 18 18 8 / **Xe** / 54 / 131.30

RADON, from radium; discovered 1900. Heaviest gaseous element, it is emitted by radium and is itself radioactive; it decays into radioactive polonium and alpha rays. This radiation makes radon useful in cancer therapy: gold needles filled with the gas are implanted into the diseased tissue.

2 8 18 32 18 8 / **Rn** / 86 / (222)

An Alias and a Taste for Togetherness

The elements commonly known as the "rare earths" are neither rare nor earths. They are soft, malleable metals—and not at all in short supply. Cerium, the most abundant, is more plentiful than tin or lead, and thulium, the scarcest, is only slightly rarer than iodine. Their misnomer arose because the oxides were at first taken for the elements themselves.

All 15 of the rare earths have two outer electrons and eight or nine in the second shell in. They vary in the electrons in the third innermost shell. But among atoms a third-shell difference is very slight indeed. Not surprisingly, then, the rare earths are a close-knit family. A mineral containing one of them contains all the others.

The rare earths are so nearly identical that separating them can involve thousands of steps; the individual elements did not become available in commercial quantities until the late 1950s. Nevertheless the family has been used industrially since the early 1900s in the form of the naturally occurring mixtures. More than a million pounds still go annually into an alloy called "misch metal," mixed metal. Combined with iron, misch metal produces cigarette-lighter flint; but its main role is in iron- and steel-making, where it absorbs impurities and improves texture and workability. A mixture of rare earths combined with carbon produces the intense carbon arc lights of Hollywood. And numerous rare-earth compounds go into high-quality glass, making it completely colorless or adding deep color, depending on the combination used.

NEODYMIUM, from *neos didymos,* or new twin; discovered 1885. In a pure form it produces the only bright-purple glass known. In a cruder state, it is used to take color out of glass and to make special glass that transmits the tanning rays of the sun but not the unwanted infrared heat rays.

60 **Nd** 144.24 — 2 8 18 22 8 2

PROMETHIUM, after Prometheus; discovered 1947; the only rare earth that has never been found in nature. Produced in nuclear reactors, radioactive promethium in an "atomic battery" no bigger than a thumbtack powers guided-missile instruments, watches and radios. Above is its oxide.

61 **Pm** (147) — 2 8 18 23 8 2

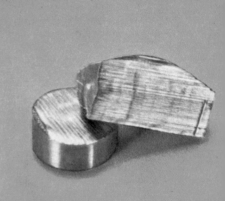

SAMARIUM, from the mineral samarskite, named for a Russian mine official, Colonel V. E Samarsky; discovered 1879 Calcium chloride crystals doped with samarium have been employed in lasers —devices for producing beams of light intense enough to burn metal or bounce off the moon

62 **Sm** 150.35 — 2 8 18 24 8 2

DYSPROSIUM, from *dysprositos,* or hard to get at; discovered 1886. Dysprosium's chief practical use is in nuclear reactors, where it serves as a nuclear "poison"—that is, it is employed as a neutron-eating material to keep the neutron-spawning atomic chain reaction from getting out of hand.

66 **Dy** 162.50 — 2 8 18 28 8 2

HOLMIUM, from *Holmia,* Latin name for Stockholm; discovered 1879. Like dysprosium, holmium is a metal which can absorb fission-bred neutrons. It is used in nuclear reactors as a burnable poison —i.e., one that burns up while it is keeping a chain reaction from running out of control.

67 **Ho** 164.93 — 2 8 18 29 8 2

ERBIUM, from Ytterby, Sweden; discovered 1843. Used in ceramics as erbium oxide to produce a pink glaze. Erbium, holmium and dysprosium are almost identical in terms of their chemical and physical properties. They vary from each other only by one electron in their third inner orbit.

68 **Er** 167.26 — 2 8 18 30 8 2

57
La
138.91

LANTHANUM, from *lanthanein,* to lie hidden; discovered 1839; highly reactive; photographed under argon. Because it gives glass special light-bending, or "refractive," properties, lanthanum is used in expensive camera lenses. Radioactive lanthanum has been tested for use in treating cancer.

2 8 18 19 9 2	58
	Ce
	140.12

CERIUM, after the asteroid Ceres; discovered 1803; most abundant of the rare earth elements. It is the chief ingredient (just under 50 per cent) of misch-metal alloy. Cerium is used in alloys to make heat-resistant jet-engine parts; its oxide is a promising new petroleum-cracking catalyst.

2 8 18 21 8 2	59
	Pr
	140.91

PRASEODYMIUM, from *prasios didymos,* or green twin (from its green salts); discovered 1885 when separated from its rare-earth twin neodymium. Together they are now used in making lenses for glassmakers' goggles because they filter out the yellow light present in glass blowing.

63
Eu
151.96

EUROPIUM, from Europe; discovered 1896. Most reactive rare earth, photographed in argon. This metal had virtually no practical use until the atomic age. But atom for atom europium can absorb more neutrons than any other element, making it valuable in control rods for nuclear reactors.

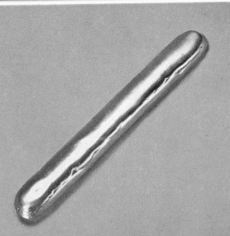

2 8 18 25 9 2	64
	Gd
	157.25

GADOLINIUM, from the mineral gadolinite, named for a Finnish chemist; discovered 1880. Falling in the middle of the rare-earth series, gadolinium divides the lighter metals, which tend to impart pliant qualities to alloys, from the heavier metals, used mostly as strengthening agents.

2 8 18 26 9 2	65
	Tb
	158.92

TERBIUM, from Ytterby, Sweden; discovered 1843; named for the town that also gave its name to three other elements: the rare earths ytterbium and erbium and the transition metal yttrium. Like all rare earths, terbium in an impure state is pyrophoric—i.e., it bursts into flame when heated.

69
Tm
168.93

THULIUM, from *Thule,* or Northland; discovered 1879. When irradiated in a nuclear reactor, thulium produces an isotope that gives off X-rays. A "button" of this isotope is used to make a lightweight, portable X-ray machine for medical use. The "hot" thulium is replaced every few months.

2 8 18 32 8 2	70
	Yb
	173.04

YTTERBIUM, from Ytterby, Sweden; discovered 1907. This element is still little more than a laboratory curiosity. Along with the other rare earths, it recently turned up in the U.S.S.R. in a mineral called gagarinite for the first astronaut. Easily oxidized, it is photographed above in argon.

2 8 18 32 9 2	71
	Lu
	174.97

LUTETIUM, from *Lutetia,* the ancient name for Paris; discovered 1907; heaviest of the rare earths. Although rare-earth alloys such as misch metal cost as low as $3.15 a pound, pure lutetium costs $1,300. With many of its chemical and physical properties unknown, it has no practical value.

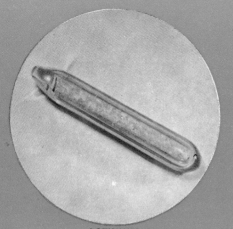

ACTINIUM, from *aktinos,* or ray; discovered 1899. Second rarest of the elements. Found in pitchblende. With a half life of 22 years, actinium decomposes into francium and helium. The minute quantity (0.037 grams) of actinium oxide shown above is encased in a radiation-resistant quartz ampoule.

2		
8	**89**	
18		
32	**Ac**	
18		
9		
2	**(227)**	

THE ACTINIDES

Elements That Decay and Finally Disappear

The actinide metals, with the heaviest atoms of all elements, end the periodic table as it is known today. Sometimes called a second rare-earth series, all have similar electronic structures and properties. All are radioactive: their decay may take moments or millions of years. All those with atomic numbers above 92, uranium, are now man-made in atom-smashers. They probably once existed in nature but have vanished because of their brief life spans.

In 1940, scientists, bombarding uranium atoms with neutrons, discovered that uranium absorbed neutrons and was transformed into the heavier elements now known as "transuranium" or "artificial." The 11 artificial elements complete the actinide series, but others may yet be found to begin a third rare-earth line in the periodic table. On these pages only 10 of the actinides are pictured: the last five do not exist in visible quantities.

THORIUM, from Thor, Scandinavian war-god; discovered 1828. Thorium can be used instead of scarce uranium as a reactor fuel because it is readily converted into uranium. Almost as abundant as lead, earthly thorium stores more energy than all uranium, coal, oil and other fuels combined.

2		
8	**90**	
18		
32	**Th**	
18		
10		
2	**232.04**	

PROTACTINIUM, from *protos,* or first; it is the parent of actinium, which is formed by its radioactive decay; discovered 1917. Third rarest of the elements, it can be prepared by modern chemical techniques at about $15,000 a gram. The small sample shown here is protactinium oxide.

2		
8	**91**	
18		
32	**Pa**	
20		
9		
2	**(231)**	

URANIUM, after the planet Uranus; discovered 1789; the heaviest atom among the natural elements. Its most common form has a half life of 4 billion years. The uranium above is shaped as a slug to insert in a nuclear reactor, where it generates neutrons to keep the chain reaction going.

2		
8	**92**	
18		
32	**U**	
21		
9		
2	**238.03**	

NEPTUNIUM, after Neptune, the planet beyond Uranus; discovered 1940. Detected first in invisible, unweighable amounts, neptunium was the first "synthetic" element made from uranium. Traces of it turn up in uranium ores, produced by stray neutrons from uranium's decay. Above is its oxide.

2		
8	**93**	
18		
32	**Np**	
22		
9		
2	**(237)**	

PLUTONIUM, after Pluto, the planet beyond Neptune; discovered 1940. Plutonium was used, instead of uranium, in several of the first atomic bombs. In one of the codes of wartime physicists, plutonium was referred to as "copper"; copper itself had to be renamed "honest-to-God copper."

2		
8	**94**	
18		
32	**Pu**	
24		
8		
2	**(242)**	

AMERICIUM, named after the Americas, by analogy with the rare earth europium; discovered 1944. Americium is produced by bombarding plutonium with neutrons. It has been made in gram quantities which, in the world of such elements, is virtually a superabundance. Above is its oxide.

2		
8	**95**	
18		
32	**Am**	
25		
8		
2	**(243)**	

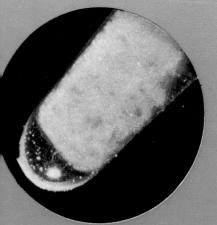

 CURIUM, in honor of Pierre and Marie Curie, pioneers in the field of radioactivity; discovered 1944. Curium, with a half life of 19 years, is a decay product of americium. The above curium hydroxide, the first known curium compound, is collected in the bottom of a tiny microcentrifuge tube.

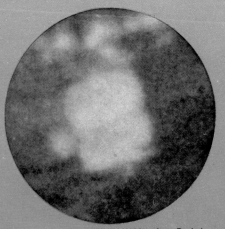

 BERKELIUM, after Berkeley, the home of the University of California, whose scientists have detected all 11 of the transuranium elements; discovered 1949. Many infinitesimal samples of berkelium have been prepared. Above is a highly magnified photograph of .00000002 of a gram of its dioxide.

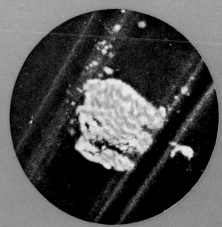

 CALIFORNIUM, after the state and University of California; discovered 1950. It was not until 1960 that californium existed in visible amounts. But the mere three tenths of a millionth of a gram of californium oxychloride above is enough to provide scientists with a veritable textbook on the element.

 EINSTEINIUM, after Albert Einstein; discovered 1952. It was first detected in the debris from the 1952 H-bomb explosion at Eniwetok in the Pacific after tons of radioactive coral from atolls in the blast area were sifted and examined. The element was later made in a nuclear reactor.

 FERMIUM, after Enrico Fermi; discovered 1953. Fermium, like einsteinium, was first isolated from the debris of the 1952 H-bomb test, having been produced from the fission of uranium. Because of its short life-span, scientists doubt that enough fermium will ever be obtained to be weighed.

MENDELEVIUM, after Dmitri Mendeleyev, who devised the periodic table; discovered in 1955. Bombarding the scantest unweighable quantities of einsteinium with helium nuclei, scientists identified mendelevium from the barest shred of evidence—one to three atoms per bombardment.

 NOBELIUM, after Alfred Nobel. A 1957 claim of discovery is disputed, but nobelium was positively identified in 1958 by a team of University of California scientists. Observations were not made on nobelium itself but on atoms of fermium 250 —"daughter atoms" produced by nobelium's decay.

LAWRENCIUM, after Ernest O. Lawrence; discovered 1961. The latest artificial element, lawrencium was made by bombarding californium with boron nuclei in a chamber fitted with a copper conveyor belt; the new atoms, one at a time, were carried to a radiation detector which identified them.

PRELUDE TO A HOLOCAUST

One of the first atomic bombs detonated, the "Fat Man" *(below),* was based on fission of plutonium. Sixty inches wide and 128 inches long, it struck Nagasaki, Japan, with a force of 20,-000 tons of TNT and destroyed seven square miles. This photograph is one of the only two pictures of the actual A-bomb ever released.

7

The Nucleus:
Enigmatic Heart
of Matter

TOWARD the end of World War I, science launched its full-scale assault on the nucleus, the innermost citadel of the atom. That such an attempt would be made had been increasingly inevitable. Many questions about the atom cried out for answers even as the scientific community was congratulating itself on a job well done in developing the exciting new concept of the atom proffered by Niels Bohr.

Bohr, as we have seen in Chapter 6, had pictured the atom as a minuscule solar system in which electrons orbited around a nucleus. But although this model accounted for many atomic phenomena, many riddles remained. What, for example, accounted for the transmutation of certain elements into others through radioactive decay? What held together the particles that made up the nucleus? What kept them from flying apart under the impulse of their mutually repellent positive charges, and thereby exploding the atom, and all matter, into bits?

Ernest Rutherford, together with some of his contemporaries, sought to answer this and other questions by new explorations in depth. Earlier studies by Rutherford had already indicated that the nucleus was extremely tiny. If one imagined, for example, that an atom was as large as a house, the nucleus would be only about the size of a pinhead. Yet nearly the whole weight of the atom must be concentrated in it, with the electrons weighing comparatively little. An imaginary nucleus the size of a pinhead would have to weigh on the order of 10 million pounds.

For his initial attack on the heart of the nucleus Rutherford chose as his weapon the tried and true high-speed alpha particles which had revealed to him the very existence of the nucleus. At one end of a long tube he placed a radioactive source of these particles. At the other end he put a screen—a small glass disk coated with zinc sulphide crystals, which sparkle when struck by alpha particles. Injecting various gases into the tube, he found that when he let in nitrogen gas the screen was dotted with those telltale flashes of light which announced the arrival of charged particles—particles with a longer range than alpha particles.

Rutherford concluded that the nitrogen atoms had been disintegrated, and that what had reached the screen were fragments from the catastrophe. He went on to deduce that he had smashed the nitrogen atom's nucleus, and that the pieces knocked off were probably the nuclei of hydrogen atoms—called protons—which exist in all atoms. In short, he had realized that ancient dream of the alchemist, the artificial transmutation of one element into another.

When Rutherford's paper on the subject was published in 1919, most physicists had to take on faith his interpretation of the welter of unknown events that might be occurring within the atom's core. Researchers craved more graphic evidence that the unseen particles were indeed smashing each other to bits. Such evidence might be forthcoming if they had some kind of apparatus—some kind of contraption in which they could watch these particles perform, like guppies in a tank.

The story of modern physics is, in large part, a story of apparatus. Today's giant accelerators, themselves veritable institutions, trace their antecedents to the shoebox-sized wood, glass and polished-brass devices of the 19th Century laboratory. Somewhere along this line of evolution was the apparatus that supplied the arena for the nuclear smashups.

A curious string of pearls

This was the cloud chamber—a glass container about as large as a pint jar—which had been invented in 1911 by a Scottish physicist, C.T.R. Wilson. He had gotten the notion for it while admiring cloud formations in the highlands; moist air masses, rolling up the slopes, suddenly bloomed into white, billowy cloud masses as they reached the thin cool air at high altitudes. At home, Wilson tried to duplicate the phenomenon by suddenly reducing the pressure of moist air in a small container. Sure enough, tiny clouds appeared. When he ionized the air, breaking up atoms into electrically charged particles, droplets of the cloud condensed around each particle. One could actually see a short straight line of droplets, like a string of pearls, tracing the path of each streaking ion.

The cloud chamber thus makes it possible actually to witness the collisions of charged particles. Tracks like smoke trails from tiny aircraft burst from the radioactive source, then shatter into a spray of other visible tracks as the invisible particles hit each other. The difficulty in using most cloud chambers is that the collision tracks can be seen only during the fraction of a second when the air pressure is being reduced.

It was not until 1925, six years after Rutherford's nucleus-smashing experiment, that the British physicist P.M.S. Blackett produced photographic evidence of the event in a cloud chamber. In the course of taking some 23,000 photographs, he caught the nucleus in the act of shattering only eight times. But the evidence was as convincing as a flash photo of startled safe-crackers at the scene of a crime.

What Blackett saw was the familiar fan-shaped spray formed by alpha particles entering the chamber, most of them abruptly ending after they had traversed their characteristic short range. One particle's track, however, suddenly forked, forming one stubby dense track that quickly ended, and another long thin track that shot clear to the end of the chamber. Study convinced Blackett that this long track was made by a proton—a single positively charged particle that had burst out of an atom's nucleus. The short thick track belonged to the rest of the nucleus, recoiling under the impact of the alpha particle.

To this day a descendant of the cloud chamber plays a part in nuclear investigation. One evening in 1951 Donald Glaser, a young physicist at

152

the University of Michigan, was musing over a glass of beer when he hit on the notion that perhaps the bubbles that foamed up in it might be related to the droplets formed in cloud chambers. He put a liquid (ether) under pressure, then periodically relieved the pressure. Elatedly he saw the familiar tracks of nuclear particles traced in bubbles as they coursed through the liquid. Glaser, in effect, had created the reverse of the cloud chamber—gas bubbles in liquid instead of liquid droplets in gas. The great advantage of using liquids is that more atoms are present in the paths of the accelerated particles, increasing the chance of collision many thousandfold. Scientists now immerse these "bubble chambers" in powerful magnetic fields that make charged particles curve in specific ways according to their charge, mass and velocity.

The cloud chamber eventually helped solve the puzzling problem of atomic weights, which, unlike atomic numbers, are rarely whole numbers. Since the nuclei of all elements were thought to be made essentially of protons, one would expect all atomic weights to come out as multiples of a proton's weight—hence as whole numbers.

The solution had been glimpsed by J. J. Thomson, discoverer of the electron, back in 1912. He was studying positively charged particles in a type of Crookes tube, using neon gas. When he applied electric and magnetic fields to bend the stream of these particles—just as he had done in measuring the electron—he got not one single deflected stream but two: a heavy stream and, beside it, a fainter one, not as sharply bent. Thomson concluded that "neon is not a single gas but a mixture of two gases, one of which has an atomic weight of about 20 and the other about 22." Perhaps it was the average weight of the two gases that accounted for neon's non-whole-number atomic weight of 20.2.

Enter the isotope

Later Thomson's protégé, F. W. Aston, using more sensitive apparatus, confirmed that neon gas was indeed made up of two types of atoms, one with an atomic weight of 20, and the other of 22—both neat and satisfying whole numbers. There appeared to be about 10 times as many lighter neon atoms as heavier ones. If a weighted average is used, the average atomic weight of neon becomes 20.2. Such mixtures of atoms were found in other elements. Atoms chemically identical with each other but with different weights were labeled isotopes. An explanation was still lacking as to how isotopes of the same element could have different weights, which went back to the same question of why the atomic weights were not whole numbers. To account for the anomaly, Rutherford and several other scientists proposed that there might be an unknown constituent in the nucleus whose presence would make for a weight difference.

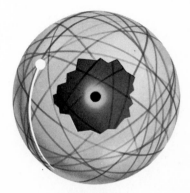

PROTIUM

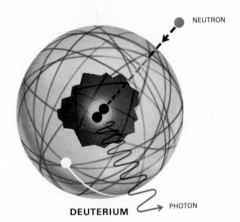

NEUTRON

DEUTERIUM   PHOTON

TRITIUM

A NEUTRON'S DIFFERENCE
The atoms above represent the three isotopes of hydrogen. Protium (*top drawing,* 99.98 per cent of atmospheric hydrogen) has one proton (black) and one electron (white ball with a tail). It is converted into deuterium *(middle drawing)* by taking a neutron into its nucleus (shown entering the nucleus along a dotted line) and emitting a photon, an energy "particle" of no charge or mass. When the process is repeated, deuterium is converted to tritium *(bottom).*

153

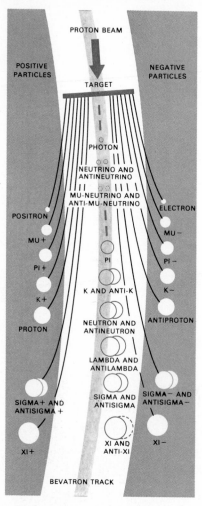

"FUNDAMENTAL" FRAGMENTS
Atomic nuclei may release 32 "fundamental" particles when a high-energy beam of protons produced in a particle accelerator slams into a target, like the one in dark blue at the top of the diagram. The eight fragments with positive charges are separated for study by a strong magnetic field that pulls them to the left. The lighter the particle, the more sharply its path is curved. The same magnet pushes the eight negative particles to the right. Physicists believe that there are 16 neutral particles, but have not yet conclusively proved the existence of the three shown above as dotted circles—the mu-neutrino and anti-mu-neutrino, and the anti-xi particle. Though most of these particles exist in free space for no more than a ten billionth of a second, certain combinations of them known as "resonances" live for no longer than a hundred thousandth of a billion billionth of a second.

Because it was presumed to carry no electric charge, this new particle was given the name neutron, and a search started for proof of its existence. Finally, in 1932, James Chadwick, one of Rutherford's disciples, filled a cloud chamber with nitrogen and exposed it to some mysterious rays known to be emitted from beryllium when it was bombarded by alpha particles. Photographs showed what were apparently nitrogen nuclei recoiling under the onslaught of mysterious blows. By measuring the recoil, Chadwick deduced that the rays causing these blows consisted of "particles of mass nearly equal to that of a proton and with no net charge." These, he guessed, must be neutrons. Scientists now had to take into consideration that, along with the protons, there were various numbers of neutrons bound into the nucleus and contributing to the weights of the various isotopes.

Theory in a raw egg

But vital questions still hung fire: what held all these particles together, and how were they arranged? According to one suggestion, the nucleus might be a system constructed somewhat like the atom itself, with the nuclear particles revolving in specific orbits, or "shells"—just as Bohr had envisioned electrons whirling around the nucleus. Another theory which has proved useful has likened the nucleus to a drop of liquid. In this scheme, the neutrons and protons behave much like the molecules in a drop of water—with a kind of attraction for each other that holds the nucleus together. These seemingly irreconcilable concepts of the shell and the liquid-drop structure of the nucleus were joined in 1953 in the "unified" theory of Aage Bohr, the son of Niels—a concept of the nucleus as a liquid in layers, like the yolk and white of a raw egg.

For all these theories, the make-up of the nucleus remains a mystery. As scientists have bombarded atoms with projectiles of ever higher velocities, they have dislodged from the nucleus not merely neutrons and protons but also a swarm of new, strange-acting particles like the clowns who keep tumbling out of the little car at the circus.

One day in 1932, in his laboratory at the California Institute of Technology, Dr. Carl Anderson was busy recording cosmic rays, those mysterious particles that come ripping to earth at tremendous velocities. He photographed what happened in a cloud chamber when a cosmic ray penetrated a lead plate and then entered a strong magnetic field. One photograph disclosed a track identical to that of an ordinary electron, except that when it curved under the influence of the magnetic field, it curved in the *opposite direction*. Anderson deduced that it was a "positive electron, which we shall henceforth contract to positron."

Positrons are born to live but briefly. The instant a positron encounters an electron, these two antithetical particles—for reasons not yet fully understood—annihilate each other to the accompaniment of a release of energy. It was this conversion of mass into energy that was forecast in Einstein's epochal equation $E = mc^2$. In the equation, E stands for energy, m for mass, and c for the fantastic speed of light, 186,000 miles per second. The energy equivalent of an electron or a positron can be computed by multiplying the weight of either—.00000000000000000-00000000009 grams (9×10^{-28} grams)—by the square of the speed of light. When dealing with atomic particles, physicists prefer to figure energy in a unit known as the Mev—a million electron volts. The suicidal clash of an electron with a positron would yield one Mev. This energy manifests itself as gamma rays.

The discovery that there was a direct antithesis to the electron confirmed, in a curious way, the essential symmetry of nuclear physics, but also added to its complexity. For *every* particle, it could now be surmised, there was likely to be an antiparticle. Carrying such speculation far out to its ultimate conclusion, physicists began to play with the notion that there is some kind of antimatter whose atoms are made up of antiparticles—antielectrons (or positrons) circulating around antiprotons. Presumably, a piece of antimatter meeting with a piece of ordinary matter would precipitate a catastrophic mutual annihilation.

A question of opposites

Is it possible that a blazing inferno of flame recognizable only as a speck in a giant telescope is actually a collision between a galaxy and an antigalaxy? Would one galaxy have a gravity anti to that of another? Scientists lack the answer to such questions; but no one can dismiss them as the improbable fancy of science-fiction writers.

The mysterious cosmic rays which first revealed the antiparticle continued to be a useful tool for science. But gradually a man-made armory of particle bombarders—cyclotrons, synchro-cyclotrons, betatrons and synchrotrons—has been amassed. Although no match for the most powerful cosmic rays, they can fire more particles at a target.

As the machines have grown, new particles have been blasted out of the atom's nucleus in an utterly bewildering proliferation. Some particles emerge only briefly, then disappear or spontaneously change into two or more completely different particles. Some were predicted theoretically before being discovered.

For example, physicists long sought for an explanation of the immensely powerful force that holds protons and neutrons together at the atom's heart. This cannot be an electrical force, for even the neutrons, which have no charge, stick together. It cannot be a gravitational pull, for gravity between particles of such minute mass would be too weak. Furthermore, experiment showed that the nuclear force, whatever it

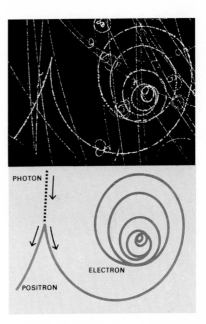

MAKING MATTER FROM ENERGY
The elaborate tracery shown in the hydrogen bubble chamber photograph above is a picture of matter being created from energy—a miniature atom bomb in reverse. The photo shows the bubbly trails which result when charged subatomic particles from the University of California's bevatron move through liquid hydrogen kept just below its boiling point. The accompanying diagram clarifies the specific paths of the newly created bits of matter: the dotted line represents the path of the high-energy gamma ray, or photon—a path that is invisible in the bubble chamber photo because the photon carries no electric charge. The curved lines represent the positron and electron produced when the photon decays. They are turned to left and right by the magnetic field that surrounds the bubble chamber.

might be, had a very short range. Then, in 1935, a Japanese theoretical physicist, Hideki Yukawa, came up with a new approach to the nuclear force problem. Yukawa's theory was that perhaps there was within the nucleus still another "elementary particle" which oscillated rapidly back and forth between the protons and neutrons, holding them together; its action might be compared to a pendulum swinging between two objects, attracting both of them to it. Yukawa calculated that his linking particle would have to weigh about 200 times as much as an electron.

Pikes Peak and a particle

The idea seemed strange, but physicists took it seriously and began hunting for the particle. In 1936, Carl Anderson, who had been exploiting cosmic rays with great success—this time atop Pikes Peak in Colorado—announced the discovery of a particle with a mass about 200 times that of an electron. He called it mesotron—later shortened to meson. It seemed intriguingly like the agent of nuclear force Yukawa had predicted. But since it did not conform in all respects with the Japanese scientist's theory, researchers went on looking.

After World War II, a British-Italian research team, C. F. Powell and G.P.S. Occhialini, who had been sending special packets of photographic film aloft in high-altitude balloons to sample cosmic rays, announced that they had found not one meson, but two. One, which was dubbed the mu-meson (muon for short), was identified as the particle Carl Anderson had discovered a decade earlier. The other was called the pi-meson (pion); and since it soon proved to have a strong affinity for both neutrons and protons, it was considered to be Yukawa's particle.

The list of fundamental particles jarred from the nucleus now exceeds 30. These include electrons, protons, neutrons, neutrinos and several kinds of mesons, along with a class of particles, heavier than the proton, called hyperons, which have three groups known as lambda, sigma and xi particles. Each one on this whole list has its antiparticle.

Some of these particles appear to serve some vital purpose within the nucleus. Without them, the equations of nuclear events do not balance properly. For example, the hunt for the elusive neutrino was pursued for a quarter of a century because unless its existence was assumed, no consistent pattern could be detected in the energy of electrons emerging from the nuclei of radioactive atoms; some unknown particle seemed to be stealing some of the energy. But the theory also said that if there *were* a neutrino, it would have no charge at all and little mass, and therefore might pass through 100 trillion miles of lead before being stopped by a collision. Thus it would be even more difficult to detect than the neutron. But in 1956, two Americans, Frederick Reines and Clyde Cowan Jr., reported that they had found the neutrino. Using apparatus set up beside a giant atomic reactor, from which such particles were believed to emerge, they had recorded the destructive evidence of collisions between neutrinos and atomic nuclei.

On the list of nuclear particles only those are included which have fairly long lives, at least for the atomic world: i.e., those having half lives averaging about one ten billionth of a second or longer. But to add to the physicists' woes, they have recently discovered several dozen so-called "resonances": particlelike entities which live for about a hundred thousandth of a billion billionth of a second.

From the welter of particles issuing from the apparently inexhaustible recesses of the atom's core, science is trying to put together some kind of theory that would account for their presence. Are they all different forms of a few particles? No one knows for sure, but most physicists believe that when a good theory does emerge, it will emerge out of the powerful ideas and equations of quantum, or wave, mechanics.

For until now we have been dealing with the fragments of the nucleus as particles only. But again, as in Chapter 6, a truer picture must take into account the dual view of matter as both particles and waves.

A new note of uncertainty

Furthermore, we must invoke a rule about atoms that has, for most physicists, removed any hope that there will ever again be a really clear-cut picture of an atom or of a nucleus. Its very name is, in fact, the principle of uncertainty. Enunciated in 1927, it was the brain child of a young German physicist named Werner Heisenberg. Briefly, it stated that there was no way at all of keeping precise tabs on an electron or *any* atomic particle. Electrons are so tiny, and light waves so relatively coarse, that to try to pinpoint an orbiting electron with light waves would be like trying to measure the thickness of a sheet of paper with a yardstick. Even if we used a gauge fine enough (and it would require an X-ray of short-wavelength), the very impact of the X-ray would disturb the course of the electron. In fact, Heisenberg demonstrated through ironclad reasoning, the more accurately the electron's position is determined, the less accurately its momentum can be measured.

Though this might seem a quibble about laboratory techniques, Heisenberg's principle had basic philosophical implications that were to revolutionize physics. For at the same time that uncertainty was making the purely negative statement that certainty about atomic particles was impossible, it had a positive side also. It was telling physicists to forget for all time their futile efforts to make exact determinations of both position and momentum at the atomic level. Instead, it told them, they should devote their energies to trying to evolve new physics. Gradually this new physics has emerged, and has been immensely successful.

A NUCLEUS IN A TEST
The role of the nuclear particle the pion is much like that of a hypothetical mother sparrow with two giant nestlings which she must keep from jumping out of the nest. Each baby bird represents a proton, while the nest represents the nucleus. Protons are electrically charged particles that tend to repel each other. Like the mother bird, the pion holds the nucleus together by jumping back and forth from proton to proton. Scientists believe that when a pion is near one of the protons it converts the proton to an electrically neutral neutron, but then when the pion swings back to the other proton the neutron reverts to its former state as proton.

Going by the name of quantum, or wave, mechanics, it is a mathematical system that largely forgets the classic preoccupation with *exact* movements of *individual* particles and worries only about the *probable* movements of particles. The mathematics of Heisenberg's probabilities, it turns out, correspond exactly with the mathematics of Schrödinger's waves (Chapter 6). Hence most scientists now view waves of matter as "probability" waves—visualizations of the rising and falling probabilities that particles will be at a given place. For example, the peaks of the waves surrounding an atomic nucleus coincide exactly with the most probable positions of an electron's path, therefore with the positions of orbits as calculated back in the early days of Bohr's atom. Transistors, superconductors, supermagnets, the powerful light-generating lasers and a host of other devices have crept out of the complex mathematical heart of quantum mechanics; they would never have emerged from the old theory of the Bohr atom.

Nevertheless, as we have seen from the present overabundance of unexplained nuclear particles, physics today is not all clear-cut understanding and superefficient mathematics. The old view of its simple discrete particles and precise planetary orbits is gone. The physicist now prefers to view the atom as a ball of energetic and uncertain fluff. The wonder is that the more clouded its structure has become, the better has been the view into its heart.

Giant Tools for Prying Secrets from a Speck

As physicists keep closing in on the elusive, deep-down identity of matter, the tools of their search get bigger and more complex. The most important and impressive are the particle accelerators, or atom-smashers. These differ in size and performance, but essentially what they all do is to load up minute particles—about one trillionth of a centimeter in diameter—with terrific energy and then hurl them at equally small subatomic targets. The resulting collisions shatter the targets into bits and pieces which provide vital clues about the structure of matter. Often, the more energy an accelerator can give its tiny projectiles, the more informative the experiment will be. Three decades of technical progress have already developed enormously complicated machines to produce ever higher energies *(pages 160-167)*. Yet it is inevitable that as the probe into the atom goes deeper, the tools of the future will dwarf even those of today.

EARLY PORTRAIT OF A PARTICLE BEAM
One of the world's first big atom-smashers, the famous cyclotron at the University of California in Berkeley, produced this beam of accelerated particles in 1939. The purple glow comes not from the beam itself (shooting from the window at left) but from the atoms of air which have been agitated by the beam's passage. This cyclotron was dismantled in 1962 because it was obsolete.

PROFILE OF A CONTEMPORARY BEHEMOTH

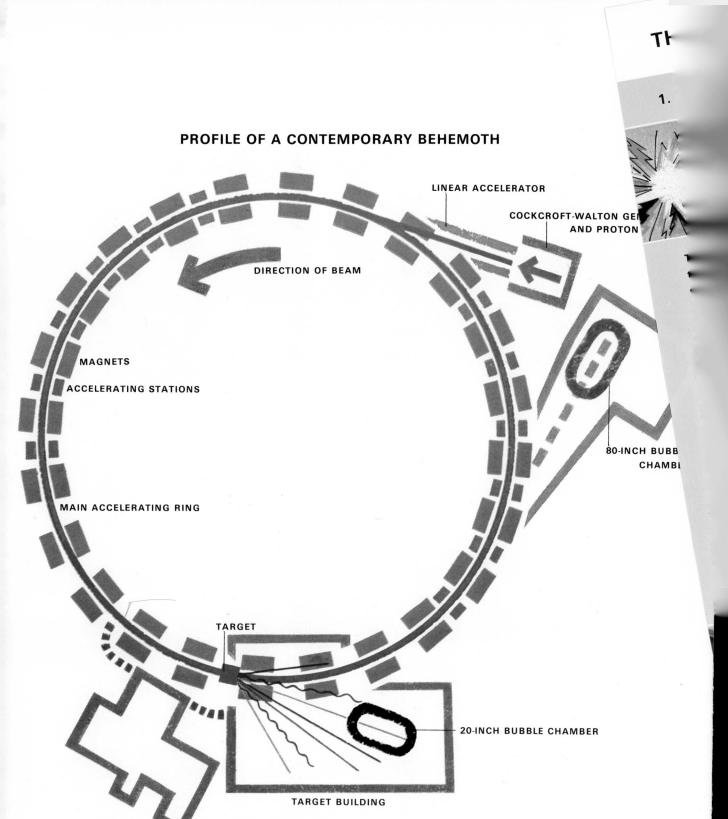

LINEAR ACCELERATOR

COCKCROFT-WALTON GE᷑
AND PROTON

DIRECTION OF BEAM

MAGNETS

ACCELERATING STATIONS

MAIN ACCELERATING RING

80-INCH BUBB᷑
CHAMB᷑

TARGET

20-INCH BUBBLE CHAMBER

TARGET BUILDING

ADMINISTRATION BUILDING

Brookhaven's alternating gradient synchrotron is shown here in diagram as seen from above. The Cockcroft-Walton generator, named for its two British inventors, produces an initial electric force which bounces protons into a linear accelerator (linac) to be speeded up before entering the main accelerator ring. The huge magnets are the brain of the AGS, shaping and controlling the beam of protrons orbiting in a vacuum around the ring. The monster's pulse is provided by 12 accelerating stations; each repeatedly speeds the beam along with synchronized electric jolts. At any one time, up to a dozen separate proton beams can be sent chasing one another around the ring. When a beam hits the target, it looses a shower of secondary particles. These are screened and directed to bubble chambers and other devices for study and evaluation.

GENERATING A CHARGE

THE FIRST BLAST of energy to get things started in an alternating gradient synchrotron (AGS) is an authoritative electrical jolt of 750,000 volts.

ELECTRIC FORCE

THE INITIAL ENERGY comes from a giant generator which produces a voltage 6,800 times greater than that provided by a normal electric outlet. At peak operation a new acceleration cycle is initiated about every 2.5 seconds.

THE COCKCROFT-WALTON generator, about 20 feet high, was originally used by its inventors as an accelerator in itself, to produce the first man-made nuclear reaction in 1932. Now it is the initial stage in newer, larger accelerators.

2. PRODUCING PROTONS

PROTON PROJECTILES start racing to target with a push from the initial electric charge. The proton cartooned actually represents trillions of particles.

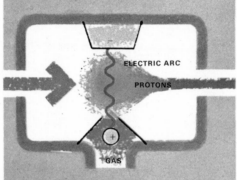

ELECTRIC ARC

PROTONS

GAS

THE PROTON SOURCE is an ionizing chamber where an electric arc *(wavy line)* produces positively charged protons from hydrogen gas. The generator's positive voltage is used to repel the protons and give them their start.

THE IONIZING CHAMBER produces its proton "bullets" by stripping away the single electrons of hydrogen atoms and leaving just the nuclei with a positive charge. The chamber, shown here with its door open, is only about a foot across.

3. STARTING THE PROTO

SUCCESSIVE JOLTS from a series alternating electric fields prod the protons through a linear accelerator. Traveling in a small round cluster, th

ALTE

PROTONS

STRAIGHT-LINE VELOCITY in the l ear accelerator is produced by 124 "dr tubes which alternate their electric fie in exact timing with the passage throu them of the protons. There is no celeration within the tubes themsel

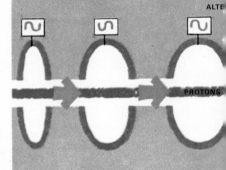

THE LINEAR ACCELERATOR is a c drical tank 110 feet long by 39 inc across. The drift tubes *(bottom cen* are positioned so the one-inch orifi through which the beam passes ar exact alignment. The tubes change f

S' ACCELERATION

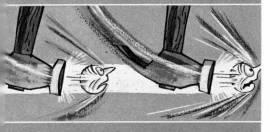

of speed up with each jolt until they are
ro- ready for injection into the circular main
av- accelerator ring at 62,000 miles per
ey second, about one third their final speed.

NATING CURRENT

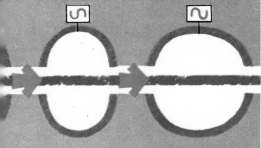

n- (hence "drift"), but between tubes the
t" protons get a new jolt of energy every
ds time the field changes *(arrows)*. When
gh they get through with this stage, the
c- protons each have been loaded with
es 50 million electron volts (Mev) of energy.

n- two-inch-thick pancake shapes to 16-
es inch watermelon shapes in order to
er) compensate for the protons' increasing
es speed. (Since air molecules would dis-
in turb the beam's passage, the whole ac-
m celeration process occurs in a vacuum.)

4. CURVING THE ORBIT AND FORMING A BEAM

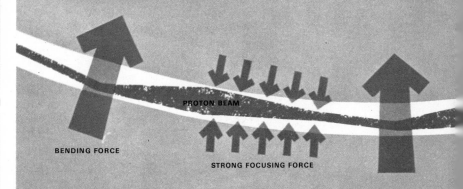

MAGNETIC TORTURE in the main accelerator ring molds the proton cluster
into a narrow beam (about the shape
of a garden hose) by squeezing it one
way and another just as a baker kneads
a lump of dough. The magnets also al-
ter the beam's course from a straight
line into a half-mile curved orbital path.

BENDING FORCE   PROTON BEAM   STRONG FOCUSING FORCE

STRONG FOCUSING ACTION of the
magnets *(small arrows)*, squeezing the
protons in different directions, is caused
by the alternating gradient system that
distinguishes the AGS from less effi-
cient synchrotrons using a non-alter-
nating, or "weak focusing," magneti
field. In all synchrotrons the magneti
force that keeps the proton beam in it
fixed orbit *(large arrows)* must increas
steadily as the beam's rising velocit
tends to widen the track of its orbi

THE MAGNETS embrace the accelerator's three-by-six-and-a-half-inch vacuum ring at even intervals around the
circumference. There are 240 magnets,
each weighing 17 tons and containing
2,800 laminations of .031-inch steel.
For stability they rest on girders ate
piles driven 50 feet into the groun
The pole face of each magnet is sp
cially curved to produce the alternati
gradients which knead the proton bea
as it travels around inside the rin

The Greatest Matter-Smasher in the World

At the Brookhaven National Laboratory near New York City sprawls the world's largest particle accelerator *(left)*. Its vastly complex equipment spreads over 20 acres, cost $33 million and requires the attention of 180 people. Much of it is underground, in a tunnel a half mile around which houses the apparatus for souping up subatomic particles to energies of 33 billion electron volts. (An electron volt—ev—is the unit of energy given to a charged particle by an electric field.)

A particle beam endowed with such high energy has two chief uses. First, it can produce new kinds of particles by the force of its collisions with target nuclei. Second, it acts as a kind of super microscope. When energized particles bounce away after impact with their target, they carry certain impressions of the characteristics of the nuclei. These impressions can be recorded, thus giving researchers an "eye" for looking inside the atom.

Most accelerators treat moving charged particles to successive, cumulative bursts of electrical energy. The technique varies with different types of atom-smashers (see Appendix). Brookhaven's behemoth is a synchrotron, which races particles called protons in a circular orbit. They are kept in line by ingenious magnets which constantly shove and squeeze the protons with changing magnetic fields, or gradients. This feature accounts for the machine's formal name, "alternating gradient synchrotron" (AGS). The operation of this unparalleled instrument of pure research is described on the following pages.

A GIANT THAT NEVER SLEEPS
This aerial photograph shows Brookhaven's vast AGS complex from about the same perspective as does the diagram at right. The circle of the main accelerator ring is 843 feet across. The 10 feet of earth atop the ring makes a natural radiation shield; the AGS poses no danger for its operators or the surrounding countryside. Researchers from all over the U.S. make such demands on the AGS that it operates on a three-shift-a-day basis.

5. SPEEDING UP THE BEAM

TOP VELOCITY, close to the speed of light, is achieved as the proton beam is kicked repeatedly through the accelerating stations positioned around the ring.

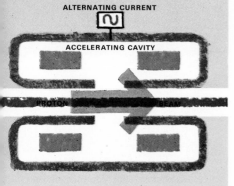

A PEAK ENERGY of 33 billion electron volts (Bev) is the sum of all the 8,000-volt kicks imparted by each accelerating station as the beam goes through the "cavity." The beam's single-orbit time is reduced from .8 to .3 microseconds.

THE ACCELERATION STATIONS are synchronized (hence the name synchrotron) to administer their accelerating jolts to the proton beam at exactly the right time despite the fact that the beam's speed is continuously increasing.

6. HITTING THE TARGET

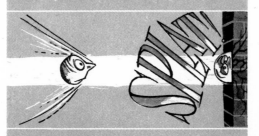

JOURNEY'S END for the protons is at the target after 300,000 orbits, a distance of 150,000 miles. From the first step the whole trip takes one second.

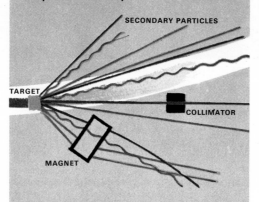

HEAD-ON IMPACT occurs as the beam is slightly bent toward a target inside the vacuum ring. The bombardment produces secondary particles which collimators, magnets and other "screening" devices then channel to the researcher.

THE TARGET, being pointed out above, is a thin blade made, in this case, of aluminum. Blades of different materials can be substituted inside the ring when experiments call for other elements to be battered by the proton beam.

7. RECORDING THE RESULTS

SHATTERED MATTER from the target consists of fragments of atomic nuclei as well as other particles which can be isolated for individual experiments.

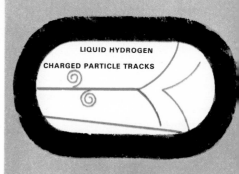

POSITIVE PROOF of the effect of impact is provided as charged particles leave tracks in a bubble chamber filled with liquid hydrogen. Particle collisions are represented by the curved lines, displaced electrons by the small circles.

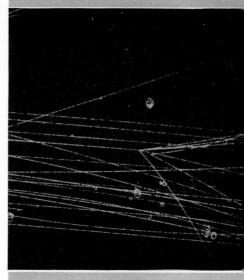

THE FINAL RESULT is a permanent visual record of particle activity in a bubble chamber after the proton beam has smacked into an aluminum target. The AGS experimenters now use about one million dollars' worth of film in a year.

10,000 FEET OF LINEAR ACCELERATOR

ELECTRON INJECTOR STATION   KLYSTRON GALLERY   ACCELERATING TUNNEL

ELECTRON GUN   ELECTRON BEAM   ACCELERATING PIPE

TWO MILES of California terrain have been scraped down and built up to provide a suitable thruway for the 10,000-foot tunnel being constructed to house Stanford's giant new linear accelerator *(top)*. Covered by 35 feet of earth will be the accelerating pipe *(red line and lower drawing)*, a four-inch copper tube which will carry the electron beams. They will be injected into the pipe by an electron gun somewhat like the one in a TV cathode tube. Unlike the AGS pre-accelerating linac, with its stationary drift tubes, the new machine will have as its accelerating force traveling radio waves of extremely high frequency. They will transport bunches of electrons down the length of the pipe, giving

At Stanford, the Newest Look in Accelerators

Not every accelerator deals with protons. Some work with electrons, which are also great aids to subatomic exploration. Electrons, with 1,800 times less mass than protons, can give more precise impressions of their atomic targets, and have provided some of the most explicit data about the atomic nucleus to date. But when electrons in the orbit of a circular accelerator are bent with too much force, they lose energy through radiation. A straight-line accelerator, on the other hand, poses no radiation problem, but presents another difficulty. In order to produce really high-energy beams the linac must have many very powerful accelerating stations strung out in a line, since each gets only a single crack at the passing beam. This requirement will be met in an extraordinary linear accelerator now being built at Stanford University in California. A marvel of electron artillery, it will be the longest (two miles) and costliest ($114 million) atom-smasher in the world. When finished in 1967 it will make today's biggest linac, also at Stanford *(right)*, look like a popgun.

166

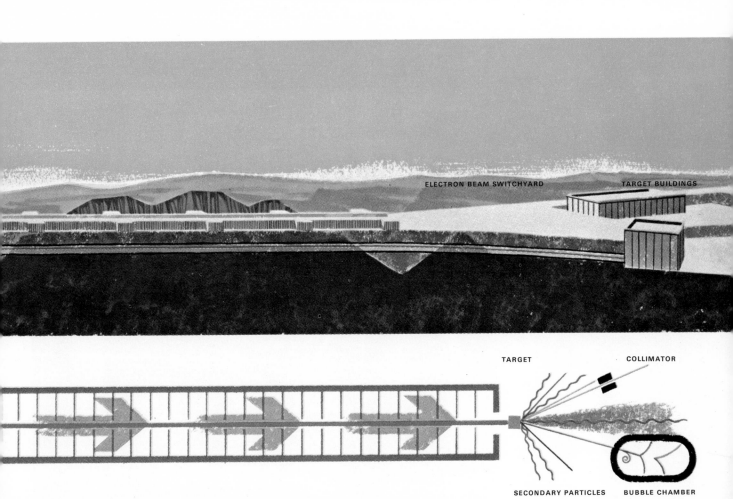

ELECTRON BEAM SWITCHYARD   TARGET BUILDINGS

TARGET   COLLIMATOR

SECONDARY PARTICLES   BUBBLE CHAMBER

them energy of up to 20 Bev. The waves will be energized by 240 radio tubes of enormous power called klystron tubes. These will be housed in the upper gallery. The design allows for 720 more tubes to be added in the future, which would boost energy output to a fantastic 40 Bev. The beam switchyard will magnetically bend the electron beam toward a variety of target sites. The vertical lines in the lower drawing represent ridges in the accelerating pipe which will control the speed of the radio waves. At the end of the pipe the beam will strike a target and jolt loose secondary particles. These can then be isolated and recorded by such devices as collimators and bubble chambers.

FORERUNNER OF A MONSTER
In current operation at Stanford is the 310-foot linac Mark III, shown while under construction in 1952. It produces about one billion electron volts. When in action, the thin accelerating pipe is hidden behind a radiation shield of concrete blocks. The success of Mark III led to the design of the new two-mile machine, which will be the equivalent of 32 Mark IIIs in a line.

167

8

The Start of an Unfinished Chain Reaction

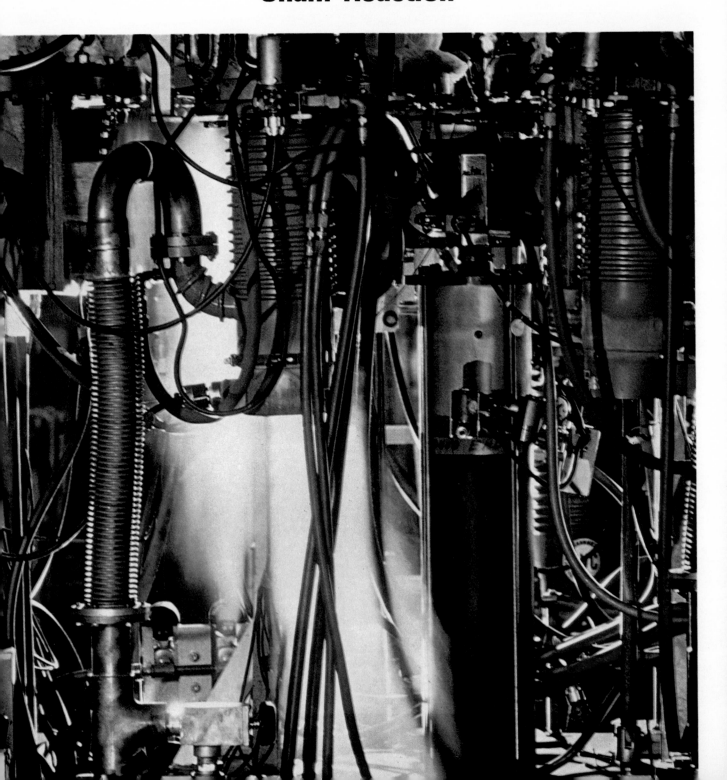

ON JULY 16, 1945, a blinding flash over the New Mexico desert heralded the emergence of the atom from the laboratory into a role which would affect the fortunes of nations and the lives of billions. It was a hurried-up debut, under the pressure of war, and it was not exactly the sort of demonstration the scientists watching it would have selected had they had their choice. But to the scientific mind, it meant the triumphant culmination of the long process of understanding—and gaining control of—the awesome energy trapped within the atom.

The process had begun around the turn of the century, when scientists first perceived that matter and energy were not separate entities but were bound up in an intimate, unbreakable relationship summed up in Einstein's deceptively terse statement, $E = mc^2$. They knew that $E = mc^2$ was no dream. The energy was there, deeply rooted in the atom. It was in fact the prime mover of the universe, the means by which the stars glowed and the sun gained its prodigious heat. The realization that man could set loose this energy right here on earth was slow in coming, for Einstein's equation was not a blueprint but simply a description of what the relationship between matter and energy would be *if* the interconversion were ever effected by man. Nevertheless, as a steady reminder of a reality underlying this equation, there was also the ever-present dribble—day after day, year after year, century after century, millennium after millennium—of energy, in the form of radiation and heat, from natural radioactive materials such as radium and thorium. These materials take respectively thousands and billions of years to lose an appreciable amount of their radioactivity, but on nature's vast time scale there is no difference between a millionth of a second and a million years. Perhaps another process could be found that would effect a release of energy in a flood instead of a dribble, although no less an elder statesman in physics than Ernest Rutherford himself said he did not think it likely.

Then, in 1938, a previously unnoticed foible of a natural element, uranium, was uncovered. In that dark and breathless time before the storm, many of Europe's leading scientists were on the move, seeking sanctuary from the racial persecution and harassment of the dictators. Gradually a number of them drifted to the United States and settled here, making this country eventually the center of atomic study. The first breakthrough, however, was achieved by two skilled radiochemists who chose to stay behind in Nazi Germany—Otto Hahn and Fritz Strassmann. They were performing an experiment of current interest in the advanced physics laboratories of the day: bombarding the element uranium with slow neutrons obtained from a radium-beryllium mixture. Similar experiments had been carried out in 1934 by the brilliant Italian physicist, Enrico Fermi, and by others in the years since. But Hahn and

ALICE AND WONDERLAND
The maze of wires and coils opposite is Alice—nickname for "Adiabatic Low Energy Injection and Capture Experiment." Alice is being used by scientists at the University of California to create minute thermonuclear reactions—not with the unbridled fury of a hydrogen bomb, but with controllable amounts of energy that they hope will power the wheels of civilization.

Strassmann got results never before observed. When they analyzed their uranium target after the bombardment, they found a trace of an element which their exhaustive tests showed to be barium—an element that weighs only about half as much as uranium. There had been no barium in the uranium sample before their tests began. If they could believe their findings, they had in effect cleft the heavy uranium nucleus down through the middle. According to the accepted theories of nuclear physics up to that time, this was about as unimaginable as splitting a brick with a peashooter.

Auguries in a manuscript

Hahn and Strassmann were perplexed. Skilled chemists that they were, they knew they had performed the experiments with care and thoroughness. But were they about to demolish their excellent professional reputations by venturing into the domain of the nuclear physicists, contradicting its guiding lights and exposing themselves to ridicule because of some laughable experimental oversight? They sent a brief report to the German scientific publication, *Die Naturwissenschaften,* announcing the findings. But at the same time they refrained from any conclusions that appeared to run counter to the views of the great physicists of the day. (In later years Hahn recalled: "After the manuscript had been mailed, the whole thing once more seemed so improbable to me that I wished I could get the document back out of the mail box.")

Then, with second thoughts still abounding, Hahn also reported his findings in a letter to the great woman physicist, Lise Meitner, for 30 years his inseparable scientific coworker; about five months earlier, she had gone to Sweden for haven from the anti-Semitic persecution of Hitler's Third Reich.

Dr. Meitner received Hahn's letter while vacationing at a seaside resort near Göteborg with her nephew, Otto Frisch, also a physicist who had fled Germany; he was then working with Niels Bohr in Copenhagen. Pondering how it could have happened that a uranium atom appeared to have been split into two atoms, each of approximately half its weight, Meitner and Frisch adapted Bohr's newly developed picture of the nucleus as a liquid drop. In this liquid-drop model, the particles in the nucleus were viewed as clinging together something like molecules in a drop of water. Such a nucleus, as we have seen in Chapter 7, is held together by a tremendous and mysterious attraction called the nuclear force, a force sufficient to overcome the electrical repulsion inherent between the close-packed, positively charged protons. It holds the uncharged neutrons in as well. This powerful nuclear force, it has been determined, operates only over a short distance—a fraction of the diameter of one of the larger atomic nuclei. Beyond this distance, the longer-

OF FISHES AND FERMIUM

The decay of a radioactive element—the process by which a nucleus loses particles or bits of energy and often changes into another element—is measured in terms of the element's "half life." This is the time it takes for one half of any quantity of the element to decay. The illustrations at right depict the radioactive decay of an isotope of fermium, fermium 256, which has a half life of three hours. If fermium is represented by 32 blue fish in a tank at noon, by 3 p.m. half of the fish will have decayed (turned gray). At 6 p.m. the number of blue fish will have been halved, leaving eight blue and 24 gray fish; and the process will continue at the same fixed rate. At 12 midnight there will be but two blue fish. Each radioactive element has its own characteristic half life: for uranium 238 it is as long as 4,500,000,000 years; for polonium 212 it is three ten-millionths of a second.

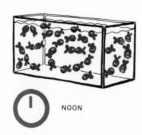

NOON

3 P.M.

ONE HALF LIFE

6 P.M.

TWO HALF LIVES

range repulsive electrical forces predominate over the nuclear force.

When an outside neutron smacks into the "liquid" nucleus, the disturbance sets the nucleus into violent oscillation. At some point it will distend into an elongated shape. When this happens, the short-range cohesive forces of the nucleus will no longer be powerful enough to hold it together. The repulsive electric forces take over and begin shoving the two ends of the nucleus farther and farther apart. It will become wasp-waisted and finally split into two halves, in much the same way that biological cells divide, although at a fantastically faster rate. It is this resemblance to biological behavior, in fact, that led Meitner and Frisch to give this nuclear process the name "fission," after the division process in cells.

They went on to reason that if fission were indeed what Hahn and Strassmann had observed, another important phenomenon should be involved: an enormous release of energy. Most of this energy emerges after the electrical forces take over and send the two new nuclei off in opposite directions at a tremendous velocity. According to the calculations made by Meitner and Frisch, the energy generated in this way would amount to approximately 200 Mev—200 million electron volts—from each tiny splitting atom.

Prelude to a journey

Frisch hurried back to Copenhagen, managing to catch Bohr just as he was about to board ship for the United States, where he was going to work for several months with Einstein himself at Princeton. When he heard Frisch's story, Bohr is reported to have slapped his forehead and exclaimed: "How could we have overlooked that so long?" He departed for America brimming with the sensational news, while Frisch rushed to his laboratory to check out the thinking which he and his aunt had done in Sweden. Even before Bohr had crossed the Atlantic, Frisch had confirmed the essence of the new theory. Like Hahn and Strassmann, he bombarded uranium with neutrons. As each neutron smashed into a uranium atom, he observed a great burst of energy, powerful enough to send the measuring devices off their scale.

Why had this escaped the notice of Fermi and others who had bombarded uranium with neutrons? Probably the answer is that almost everyone had followed in Fermi's footsteps after his initial splitting of the uranium atom in 1934, and Fermi had mistaken the radioactive uranium fragments for superheavy atoms lying beyond uranium in the periodic table. This had set off a race among physicists in many lands to find new atoms of elements 93, 94 and beyond.

There had been another near-miss on the discovery of fission by an American. At the University of California in 1936, young Philip H. Abel-

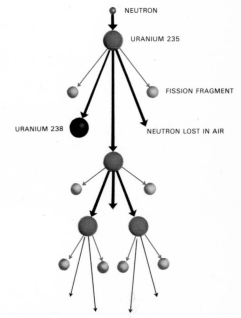

A-BLAST OR SLOW-BURN
Atomic fission, whether it results in the blast of a bomb or the slow-burn of a reactor, is based on a chain reaction, diagramed above. A neutron *(top)* hits a U-235 atom which produces fission fragments which form barium and krypton *(gray)* and as many as three new neutrons *(black arrows)*. These neutrons may (1) be captured by a U-238 atom and produce plutonium; (2) get lost in the air without being captured; or (3) strike another U-235 atom to begin the process again. When the number of neutrons lost equals the number generated, a self-sustaining chain reaction occurs. Very rapid build-up of neutrons may lead to an uncontrolled reaction, as in a nuclear explosion.

9 P.M.

THREE HALF LIVES

MIDNIGHT

FOUR HALF LIVES

171

son, just beginning his scientific career, had split the uranium atom, but did not recognize what he had done. Nevertheless, at the same time Hahn and Strassmann made their epochal experiment, Abelson was just putting together apparatus which would have identified the uranium fission fragments and captured the honor of discovering fission for the United States. It was only by a series of accidents that atomic energy was kept out of the hands of man in the critical years preceding World War II.

The news that Bohr transmitted from Meitner and Frisch spread rapidly through the growing community of foreign physicists gathering on U.S. soil. By this time—January 1939—the great Fermi himself, fed up with the Italy of Benito Mussolini, had arrived to take up a post at Columbia University. Fermi was at first taken aback when he learned of his own near-miss, but the quick mind of this quiet genius rallied to seek out further implications of nuclear fission. Billions of times more neutrons than had been mustered in the laboratory would be required before a fission reaction could even match the power of a flashlight. With his deep knowledge of the nucleus, Fermi speculated that perhaps the fission process itself might cause additional neutrons to be hurled out of the splitting nuclei. The new neutrons might go on to split more nuclei and in instants create generations of flying neutron projectiles within the mass of uranium. The term "chain reaction" was applied to this phenomenon.

A world "headed for grief"

The hypothesis caused a great stir among Fermi's fellow scientists, for if it proved out, it promised a release of energy such as man had never before achieved by his own devices. It was, in fact, quickly and dramatically verified, first by a French research team and soon thereafter by a number of scientists working independently in the U.S. In a laboratory at Columbia, the Hungarian physicist Leo Szilard and his partner, the Canadian Walter Zinn, set up a simple experiment that would disclose —by flashes of light on a television tube—whether any neutrons were being emitted from the fissioning uranium. Szilard subsequently recalled the occasion:

"If flashes of light appeared on the screen, that would mean that neutrons were emitted . . . and this, in turn, would mean that the large-scale liberation of atomic energy was just around the corner.

"We turned the switch and we saw the flashes.

"We watched them for a little while and then we switched everything off and went home.

"That night there was little doubt in my mind the world was headed for grief."

FISSION: AN ATOMIC GOLIATH FELLED BY A TINY NEUTRON

The portly uranium atom—or even portlier plutonium atom—can be cleft in two by the blow of a single neutron. In this fission process (depicted in the cartoon sequence at right), the mass of the fission products is not equal to that of the original atom—some of the mass has been converted to energy. When the small bit of energy from one atom's fission is multiplied by the enormous number of splittable atoms in a few pounds of uranium, the result is energy enough to blow a city to bits. But an even more high-powered atomic permutation is that of nuclear fusion, a process which is depicted in the margin down the side of the opposite page.

When a fast-moving neutron bowls into the nucleus of a heavyweight uranium 235 atom *(above left)*, the nucleus becomes distended

. . . and begins to "oscillate," contorting into squat and tallish shapes. But the strain of the added particle is too much and soon rends the nucleus

The fact that neutron emission had been observed did not necessarily mean that an atomic bomb was in the offing. But soon the small community of foreign-born scientists began to exercise voluntary censorship over the publication of their work, and Fermi went to Washington and broached to U.S. Navy officials the possibility that the United States might begin work developing atomic energy. He was politely received with expressions of mild interest and just as politely ushered out with the request that he keep the officials informed.

Then, by the early summer of 1939 alarm seized the foreign-born scientists. With their special sensitivity to the omens of events abroad, they were quick to assess reports from Europe that the leading German researchers were disappearing one by one into the laboratories of the Kaiser Wilhelm Institute in Berlin. There were, moreover, reports that quantities of uranium from Czechoslovakia's rich mines were funneling into the same place.

Finally, in July, the irrepressible Szilard, with his flair for the right gesture, hit upon the decisive way to sound a warning loud and clear. Joined by his fellow Hungarian physicist Eugene Wigner, he persuaded the great Einstein to send a letter to President Roosevelt. The letter, drafted in consultation between Einstein and Szilard, pointed out that recent work by Szilard, Fermi and others indicated that a nuclear chain reaction might be possible, and suggested that the government provide funds to speed up fission experiments. A grim note of prophecy pervaded the communication: ". . . it may become possible to set up a nuclear chain reaction in a large mass of uranium, by which vast amounts of power and large quantities of new radium-like elements would be generated. . . . It appears almost certain that this could be achieved in the immediate future. This new phenomenon would also lead to the construction of bombs, and it is conceivable—though much less certain—that extremely powerful bombs of a new type may thus be constructed. . . ."

It still took six months of agitation by the foreign-born scientists to get the mills of Washington to grind out $6,000 to enable Fermi to buy some graphite he said he needed to build something he called a "pile," whatever that was.

The uses of a squash court

And because of one thing or another, it took almost three years and millions of dollars before Fermi and his team assembled on December 2, 1942, in an abandoned squash court at the University of Chicago and slowly pulled out a control rod that set off the first self-sustaining chain reaction in history. This extraordinary event took place within Fermi's so-called pile: a simple stack of intermixed blocks of graphite, uranium oxide and pure uranium.

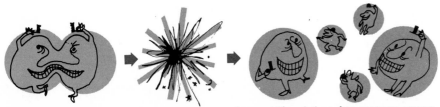

in two. This sundering, or "fission," takes place with a burst of released energy, and from the process two lighter nuclei (known as "fission fragments") and three free neutrons emerge. When a U-235 nucleus is split, the fission fragments are often nuclei of barium and krypton.

FUSION: A HOT AFFAIR BETWEEN TWO HYDROGENS

Fusion is essentially the opposite of fission: two light nuclei are "welded" together to form one heavier nucleus (as illustrated below). The fused nucleus, however, is not quite so heavy as the two light ones taken together—some mass is "lost" or converted into energy. Thus fusion, like fission, releases enormous energy, but it occurs only at ultrahigh temperatures, such as those in an atomic blast. The practical use of fusion power awaits the development of some means of sustaining H-bomb temperatures inside a power plant.

In a fusion reaction two atomic lightweights—the hydrogen isotopes deuterium and tritium—collide while in the superheated state of plasma.

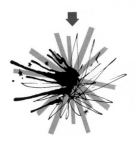

As the protons and neutrons of the two nuclei are packed into one new nucleus, energy is released as some of their total weight is lost.

Finally, a surplus neutron is cast out and a stable helium nucleus emerges as the end product of this torrid thermonuclear change-over.

Even with an atomic pile in operation, the question of whether an atomic bomb could be built was far from settled. Great obstacles still lay ahead. The real "secret" of the bomb lay within the peculiar nature of uranium atoms. Niels Bohr and an American associate, John Wheeler, had already made theoretical studies at Princeton which indicated that it was not the common isotope of uranium, with an atomic weight of 238, that was doing the fissioning under slow neutron bombardment, but rather a lighter isotope, uranium 235. The latter is normally found in nature intermixed with uranium 238 in the proportion of about one part in 140. Since the two isotopes are chemically identical, the U-235 wheat could best be winnowed from the U-238 chaff by a physical process that capitalized on the three-unit difference in mass.

Scientists in the Manhattan Project (as the bomb-building program was called) tried out a number of different techniques. The one that proved ultimately most successful was the gaseous diffusion process. This involves making a gaseous compound of uranium called uranium hexafluoride and pumping it against a barrier consisting of plates pierced with billions of tiny holes less than a millionth of an inch in diameter. According to a rather complex principle of physics, the molecules containing the lighter atoms of U-235 tend to move through the holes slightly more readily than those bearing the heavier U-238. This process, repeated in thousands of stages, gradually filters out a uranium hexafluoride gas that has a more-than-90 per cent concentration of U-235 atoms. For the atomic bomb program, a gigantic gaseous diffusion plant was built at Oak Ridge, Tennessee, at a cost of half a billion dollars.

A parental role for uranium

Meanwhile, however, physicists had hit upon another fissionable material. It was not to be found in nature, but it might be obtained as a by-product of uranium fission in a reactor such as Fermi's. If a great many neutrons were released from fissioning U-235 atoms, they would act upon nonfissionable U-238 in such a way as to transmute it into an artificial element called neptunium. Half this neptunium would spontaneously decay within 2.3 days into yet another element, plutonium, which could be extracted chemically from its parent uranium. It turned out that plutonium was even more fissionable than U-235 in a fast neutron reaction such as the atomic bomb's.

The production of plutonium now became a priority matter in the atomic bomb program, for the U-235 separation process looked slow and complicated. Three huge reactors were constructed on the banks of the Columbia River at Hanford, Washington. Each reactor was designed to produce approximately half a pound of plutonium per day. To carry away the tremendous heat developed in these reactors, cold water from

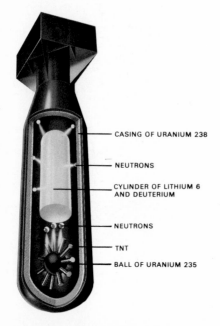

CASING OF URANIUM 238

NEUTRONS

CYLINDER OF LITHIUM 6 AND DEUTERIUM

NEUTRONS

TNT

BALL OF URANIUM 235

THERMONUCLEAR TRIPLE-THREAT
The H-bomb is a three-staged, "fission-fusion-fission" device. As illustrated above, its detonation is begun by exploding charges of TNT which blow enough U-235 together to start an uncontrolled chain reaction. The sudden shower of neutrons *(medium blue)* and ultrahigh temperature from the resulting atomic blast act on lithium 6 and deuterium atoms in the central cylinder—the lithium is converted to tritium which, mixing with deuterium at ultrahigh temperatures, forms plasma. The plasma particles instantly undergo fusion to form helium 4 in a "thermonuclear" blast which liberates even more neutrons *(white)*. Bombarding the inner U-238 jacket of the bomb *(light blue)*, these cause a final fission reaction to top off the awesome blast.

the mighty Columbia was pumped through them and back into the river.

For fission to take place spontaneously in either U-235 or plutonium, the piece of material must exceed a certain size, or "critical mass." If the chunk is too small, too many neutrons leak out of its sides before they encounter a fissionable atom. The method devised for setting off the bomb was to exceed the critical mass either by bringing two or more pieces of fissionable material together very quickly, or by compressing a hollow ball of it. Charges of conventional explosives within the bomb are usually used to perform this deed.

Debut in the desert

After five years of frantic work, comprising the erection of three secret towns, the mobilization of half a million people and an expenditure of two billion dollars, the world's first fission bomb was detonated atop a steel tower on a well-guarded stretch of desert near Alamogordo, New Mexico. It was a massive device weighing four tons, whose violent heart was a glistening sphere of plutonium the size of a baseball. A powerful explosive charge squeezed the hollow sphere until the critical density for a self-sustaining chain reaction was reached. Then, in less than one millionth of a second, the solid metal was converted into a multimillion-degree blast of hot gas, as though a bit of the interior of the sun had suddenly been brought to earth.

The bombs over Hiroshima and Nagasaki fulfilled their fearful purpose and hastened the end of the war. The deed done, most of the scientists and engineers on the Manhattan Project were happy to return to teaching, pure research or industry. Experiments progressed on converting the chain reaction to the beneficent function of producing electric power; in time, power-producing reactors were placed in operation in Britain and in certain high-cost power areas of the United States. Medical science benefited from the new profusion of radioactive isotopes, which were found to be useful both as a source of rays to treat malignancies and as "tracers" that could be followed with instruments as they coursed through the body's organs. Industry also used them as tracers, and even as a means of altering the characteristics of certain materials, such as plastics. The effect of radiation in causing genetic mutations, though generally considered one of the most deplorable aspects of the atomic age, occasionally found beneficial uses, such as in the development of a better strain of corn.

But, as we now know, the optimistic notion that atomic energy might be permanently retired to a peaceful role, exclusively dedicated to the bettering of human life, was a short-lived illusion. The heightening tensions of the cold war soon made necessary another assemblage of talent and manpower for the building of bombs. And this time the mobiliza-

A HOT HALO OF HYDROGEN
The seemingly solid sun is actually a ball of opaque, gaseous plasma, chiefly hydrogen. Its inner core is in a constant state of fusion, hydrogen being converted into helium with the release of immense stores of heat and light. Ordinarily the gaseous nature of the sun is invisible to the naked eye, but in a solar eclipse *(above)* its plasma halo is revealed.

tion was based on an awareness of an even more hellish source of energy.

Until well into this century, physics concerned itself with the three states in which matter is commonly found on earth—solid, liquid and gas. But it is estimated that a preponderance of the material of the universe exists in yet a fourth state, a violent material that is comparatively rare in human experience. We call it plasma, a name given it in 1920 by one of the early explorers of its properties, the Nobel Prize-winning American scientist Irving Langmuir.

As noted earlier in these pages, the state of a given substance under a given pressure depends directly on its temperature. As the temperature goes up, ice becomes water and water steam. Eventually, if very great heat is applied, the movement of the H_2O molecules becomes so violent that they start smashing themselves into electrically charged ions. This ionization is actually the same process that we observed, in Chapter 6, in the gases within J. J. Thomson's Crookes tubes. It is the door to the fourth state of matter.

Plasma, then, is a swarming mass of hot, electrically charged particles —free electrons carrying a negative charge, and positively charged ions, the whole being electrically neutral. Some substances require less heat than others to ionize, but the phenomenon usually does not begin until temperatures reach at least 5,000° F. or 6,000° F., and it is not really going full blast until 100,000° F. Even then, the particles keep recombining spontaneously; thus there are generally neutral atoms along with the charged particles of the plasma.

The raw material of stars

Plasma pervades the universe in various degrees of concentration. It is the raw material of which the stars are made, and it fills the space between all celestial bodies with a thin matrix that throbs and pulsates with strange waves and currents. Except in stars, its consistency is thinner than any vacuum that man has been able to create on earth.

Despite the fierceness associated with its fiery temperature, plasma is almost too delicate to exist in this cold and narrow corner of the universe we call earth. Here it is usually found only in such inhospitable places as the heart of lightning bolts, the aurora borealis, and in electric arcs. In ordinary earthly circumstances, plasma particles in their frantic movement dash into the sluggish molecules of their colder surroundings and lose their energy. Nevertheless, so full of portent for man's future is this unearthly state of matter that its investigation has become in recent years one of the largest research programs in the physical sciences.

As long ago as 1920, scientists began to assume that some sort of nuclear reaction must be going on within the plasma in the blazing mass of the sun. Otherwise how could one explain its immense and long-term

ISOTOPES TO IONS TO ENERGY

The diagrams at right depict (1) the isotopes of hydrogen; (2) their ionization in plasma; and (3) the fusion of their plasma ions in thermonuclear reactions. The ordinary hydrogen atom *(far left)* has one proton, one electron and no neutrons. With two neutrons in its nucleus it is known as tritium; with but one neutron it is called deuterium. The gray-tinted illustration in the middle shows the chaotic movement of tritium and deuterium nuclei in the plasma state: at the ultrahigh, or "stellar," temperatures of plasma, electrons jump their orbits, leaving the nuclei on their own as positive ions. In the diagrams opposite, two kinds of plasma fusion reactions are shown: above, two deuterium ions (D) fuse to form either a helium isotope (He³) plus a neutron (N) and 3.3 Mev of energy, or a tritium ion (T) plus a proton (P) and four Mev. In the bottom diagram, deuterium and tritium ions fuse to form a different helium isotope (He⁴) plus a neutron and 17.6 Mev of energy. The Mev, a standard measure of nuclear energy, is a million electron volts; interms of worldly energy a struck match gives off one million billion Mev.

176

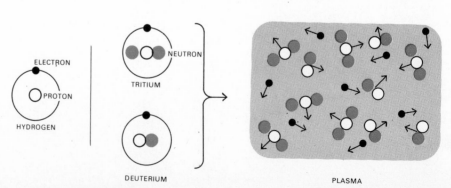

ELECTRON

PROTON

HYDROGEN

NEUTRON

TRITIUM

DEUTERIUM

PLASMA

energy production? Professor Hans Bethe, a soft-spoken theoretical physicist who was born in Alsace-Lorraine and like so many others left Europe when Hitler rose to power, proposed two possible sets of reactions as the mechanism. In the steps of the reactions the fusing elements exchange mass for energy, and five billionths of this energy, in the form of solar rays, is intercepted by the earth.

A terrifying but tantalizing thought arose: could the sun's natural fusion reaction somehow be artificially duplicated on earth? According to further elaborated theory, one such "thermonuclear" reaction would release some three and a half times as much energy per pound as would a uranium fission reaction. But burgeoning thermonuclear research immediately came up against a knotty problem. In the sun's compressed core, ordinary hydrogen ions fuse together at an appreciable rate, but such a reaction on earth would be unusably slow. Fortuitously, however, it turned out that there are two isotopes of hydrogen, called deuterium and tritium, which fuse speedily at lower temperatures. Deuterium occurs in nature combined with oxygen in so-called "heavy water," and tritium can be produced by bombarding the element lithium with neutrons from an atomic reactor.

By 1954, the U.S. government had built a mammoth plant on the banks of the Savannah River to manufacture materials for a hydrogen bomb. Two years earlier the first full-fledged "thermonuclear device" had been detonated on Elugelab Island in the Pacific; the ensuing explosion completely wiped the island off the map. Although the details are still secret, it is known that this thermonuclear device and the weapons that followed it involve essentially a sequence of three reactions: fission, fusion, and fission again. In the first stage a powerful atomic bomb is set off to generate the heat for fusion and, at the same time, to give off neutrons which go on to interact with a lithium compound, lithium deuteride, to produce tritium. In the second phase, deuterium and tritium fuse together, forming helium and releasing more neutrons of very high energy. Finally, these neutrons cause a casing of uranium 238 to fission. It is this last step which not only accounts for half to two thirds of the bomb's entire energy release, but also produces the widespread, lethal fallout of "dirty" nuclear weapons.

A potent cupful of tap water

Like research on fission, the study of fusion got its preliminary boost from military urgency but soon responded to the challenge of peaceful application. As scientists learned more about how the sun and stars develop their fantastic energies from the fusion of various ions in plasma, they looked upon the creation of a sustained (and controlled) fusion reaction as the source of practically unlimited energy that could be gener-

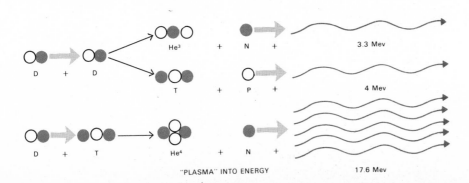

"PLASMA" INTO ENERGY

ated from fuel virtually as limitless as the waters of the ocean. For the deuterium in a cupful of tap water packs as much potential power as a full gas tank in an automobile.

For a dozen years, the question of how to achieve controlled fusion has preoccupied thousands of experimenters the world over. The United States, the Soviet Union, Great Britain, France, Germany and Japan have all mounted ambitious programs. Before 1958, almost all the various national efforts were top-secret. But one by one, the researchers ran afoul of the same difficulties, and many of the barriers of secrecy were dropped by common consent, in the hope that the combined efforts of international science might eventually lick the problem. Now the quest for controlled fusion represents one of the world's foremost examples of international scientific cooperation.

As in the H-bomb, the object in controlled fusion is to get hydrogen nuclei to fuse together to form helium or tritium nuclei, in the process generating the tremendous heat necessary to keep the reaction going. In the bomb, the nuclei are rammed together by the brute force of an atomic fission explosion. Since it is obviously out of the question to set off atomic bombs in a laboratory, science had to look for other means to raise temperatures up to the hundred million degrees or more that would "ignite" the fusion fuel.

The problem of containment

The means eventually called upon was magnetism, which could both heat the plasma and contain it once it was heated. The containment is the hard part. There is no earthly material that can be kept at more than a few thousand degrees without melting. At such a relatively frigid temperature, the wall of a material container would instantly chill to useless sluggishness any plasma particles that came in contact with it, thus stopping the reaction before it could get properly started. But if the plasma can be held within the invisible boundaries of a magnetic field, it need never touch material walls.

The simplest approach to controlled fusion called for plasma to generate its own magnetic field and thus to confine itself. This technique exploits what is known as the "pinch" effect. The scheme was to pump electricity through a column of plasma in a tube. Just as happens when current passes through a wire, the electricity sets up rings of magnetic force lines like rubber bands around the plasma column. The lines would tend to squeeze the column into a tighter core and away from the walls of the tube. Early experiments achieved this effect at first; but as soon as it got good and pinched, the plasma column would always start wiggling and bending until the kinks touched the walls and cooled the plasma. It was a little like trying to stand a shoelace on end. A number of other

A "MAGNETIC BOTTLE" FOR THE FURY OF FUSING NUCLEI

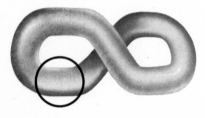

TAMING A TEMPEST OF PLASMA

To tap the tremendous power of atomic fusion, plasma physicists have devised a figure-eight-shaped "stellarator" *(above)*. The circled area is represented in detailed cross section below. In this device, plasma is "pinched" into a thin stream by means of large electrical coils, which generate strong parallel magnetic lines of force. The charged plasma particles, usually chaotic, are thus tamed and move in small spirals around the magnetic lines. But even the best of these "magnetic bottles" leaks—the plasma kinks, buckles and twists out of its spirals to touch the sides of the stellarator. When this happens the plasma cools down from the 180 million degrees needed to sustain fusion, and the process comes to a halt. So far no controlled fusion reaction has been contained for more than a fraction of a second. But scientists keep doggedly building better bottles.

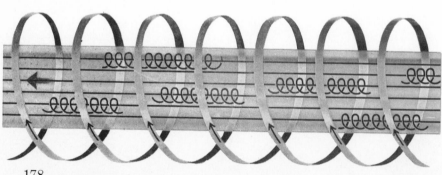

COILS OF PLASMA PARTICLES

MAGNETIC LINES OF FORCE

OUTER ELECTRICAL COILS

"magnetic bottles" have since been tried, employing a variety of ingenious techniques. But the restless plasma has always shown just a little more ingenuity in finding new ways to wriggle out of them.

Most fusion scientists are only cautiously optimistic that they will ever manage to achieve simultaneously the effective containment and heating of plasma. Nevertheless, with each passing year, researchers make a little more progress in improving their machines, understand a little more of what is going on, get a little hotter temperature, a little better containment. And a valuable concomitant of this understanding is added knowledge of other uses to which plasma may some day be put.

One fascinating line of thought which has spawned a whole new technology is called *magnetohydrodynamics* (mercifully shortened to MHD). Strictly defined, MHD is the study of the dynamic effects of magnetic fields upon electrically conducting fluids (since it flows, a plasma is defined to be a fluid). Though controlled fusion itself may be a long way off, it is quite possible that, through MHD, plasma may prove useful in improving electricity-generating techniques which employ conventional fuels. MHD principles are also likely to be used in the electric rocket engines that will some day be used to propel spacecraft. Electromagnetic fields would shove the plasma rapidly out the rear of the rocket nozzle, thus propelling the spacecraft forward. Moreover, when a spacecraft returns to earth's atmosphere, it generates a plasma around itself as it dissipates its tremendous speed among the molecules of the air. Scientists have, in fact, been studying the idea of equipping a spaceship with powerful new superconducting magnets which would "push" upon the plasma outside and thus help brake and support the ship in the course of its plummeting to earth.

But despite all the ideas abounding, scientists still have only a meager understanding of this fourth state of matter called plasma—far from enough to inspire real confidence that this tenuous but fiery stuff can be tamed to man's will.

A threshold for the future

And even if man does succeed in unlocking the energy of fusion, he will still be only on the threshold. In all the reactions yet achieved, man has been able to tap but a small fraction of a per cent of the atom's potential energy, the slim by-product of the rearrangement of a few neutrons and protons. If he could convert whole particles into energy in a controlled and directed manner, man could extend his now puny strength literally to astronomical proportions. There is little that would not then be conceivable for him to accomplish—from changing climatic conditions on his planet to shoving other planets into new orbits around the sun.

When we look at the brief span—less than the average lifetime of a man—during which human intelligence has succeeded in penetrating into the heart of the atom and wresting from it a fraction of its power, it is difficult to set a limit on what could be achieved in a few more life-times. The spectacular advances in science during recent decades have far exceeded anything that scientists like Rutherford ever thought possible. But, of course, this man who first sighted the strange loneliness of the nucleus deep within the kingdom of the atom had no inkling of the incredible complexity—and the glittering possibilities—of the tiny citadel he first stormed. The impenetrable billiard ball has been replaced by an utterly baffling community of particles whose nature and interactions continually confound theory. When the atom's innermost secrets finally fall—as fall they must—who can say what possibilities may then be exposed?

Whatever discoveries may lie ahead, it is likely that Einstein's characterization of the world of science, almost a quarter of a century ago, will continue to hold true: ". . . whoever has undergone the intense experience of successful advances made in this domain is moved by profound reverence for the rationality made manifest in existence. By way of the understanding he achieves a far-reaching emancipation from the shackles of personal hopes and desires, and thereby attains that humble attitude of mind towards the grandeur of reason incarnate in existence, and which, in its profoundest depths, is inaccessible to man."

Radiation:
A Key That Opened
the Atomic Age

Around the turn of this century there occurred a radical change in man's ideas about the structure of matter. A major role in this revolution was played by two discoveries in the field of radiation. In 1895 Wilhelm Roentgen chanced upon a kind of radiation completely unlike the familiar rays of heat and light. His X-rays, made by an electric current in a vacuum tube, were invisible and unfelt, yet could make extraordinary pictures on film (opposite). The next year brought an even bigger discovery: radioactivity. This is a property of certain elements whose atomic nuclei are relatively unstable and spontaneously throw off radiation in the form of energy or matter. The contribution of X-rays and radioactivity in founding the modern era of science was enormous: their dangers, long unrealized, have proved to be equally immense. Now, for both good and bad, these forces of radiation are clearly fixed as a prime factor of the atomic age.

REVELATIONS OF AN X-RAY
The public's first awareness of X-rays and the fact that they could penetrate flesh to make skeletal images on film came through photographs such as this one taken in February 1896 by Professor Michael Pupin of Columbia University. The black spots in the picture opposite are not faults in the film—they are bird shot embedded in the subject's hand in a hunting accident.

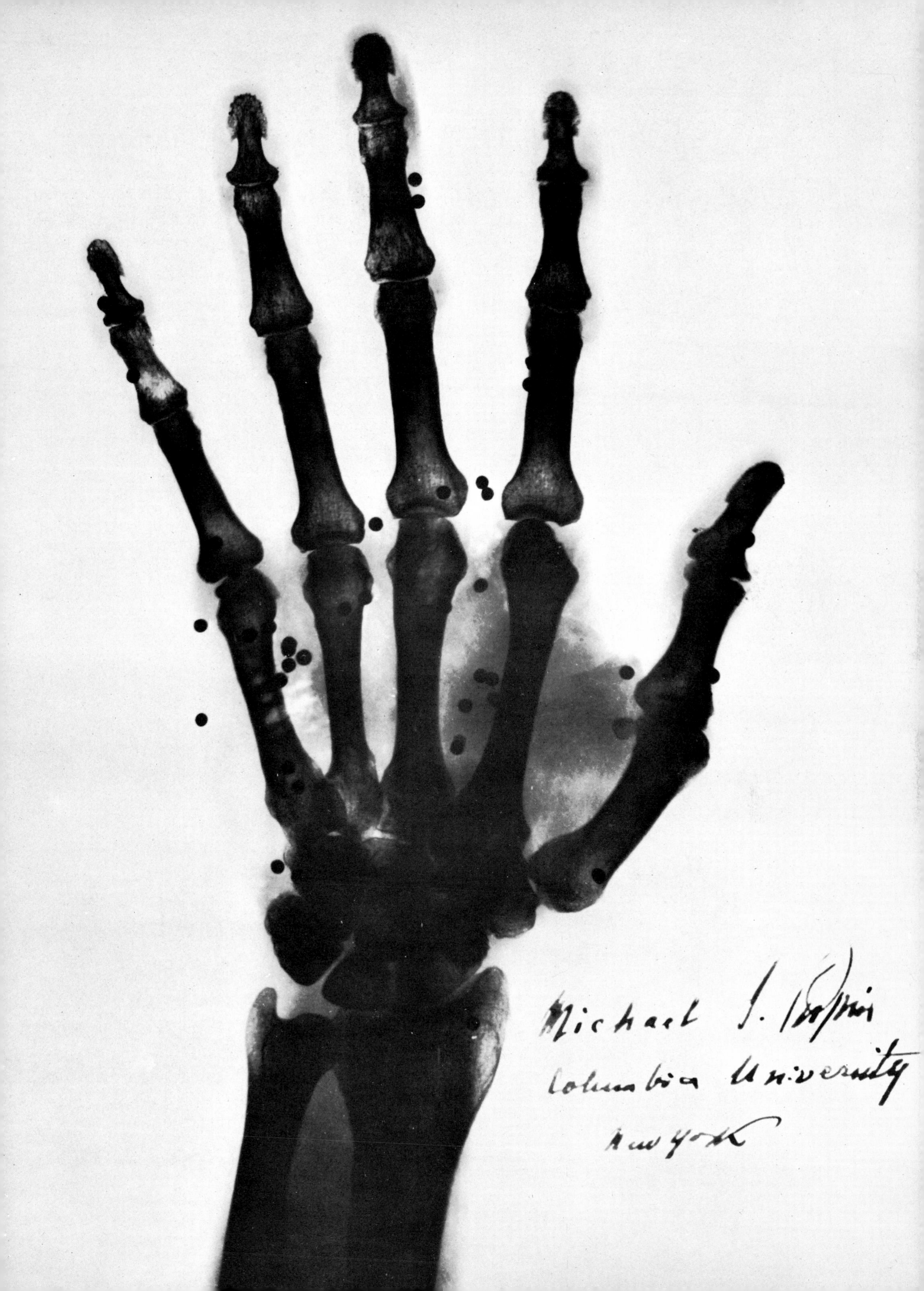

Michael I. Pupin
Columbia University
New York

THAT DELICIOUS MOMENT

WHEN YOU FIND YOU ARE TO TAKE INTO DINNER THE GIRL WHO YESTERDAY REFUSED YOU.

In X-Rays, a Source of Amusement and Wonder

The extraordinary new X-rays of Professor Roentgen (*below*) took Europe and America by storm. The idea of seeing the unseeable was irresistible, and since the cathode-ray tube in which they were produced was a common item of laboratory equipment, hundreds of scientists became X-ray "experts" overnight. Ghostly pictures of hands and feet appeared in newspapers everywhere, as well as in jokes and cartoons (*left*). Ignorance of the subject was widespread. A German newspaper editor was so terrified after seeing an X-ray of his head that he could not sleep for nights, while a London firm advertised "X-ray-proof underwear—no lady safe without it."

Many doctors, however, immediately put X-rays to valuable work (*opposite*) and other ingenious uses were found (*below opposite*). The trouble was that few people in those early days realized how dangerous X-rays and other kinds of radiation can be (*pages 188, 189*). It was some years before the world learned the full impact of Roentgen's "new kind" of ray.

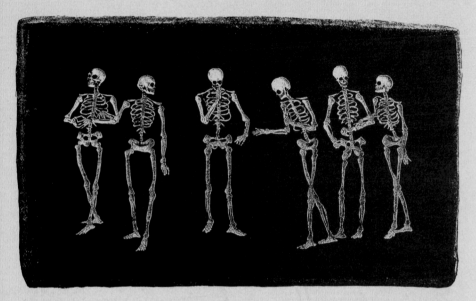

FOR those of our readers who like to get at the inside facts of a case we publish these companion pictures. They are interesting as showing the possibilities of the art of the future when developed by advanced photography. We have selected a well-known drawing from LIFE as better illustrating our point.

POKING FUN AT A NEW FAD
The public's fascination with X-rays proved a great source of fun for publications both in Europe and the U.S. The American humor magazine *Life* took this tongue-in-cheek view of X-ray photography in 1896. Interest in the new rays ran so high that within a year of Roentgen's discovery more than 1,000 books, articles and pamphlets had been published on the subject.

IMPACT OF A NEWS ITEM
The New York Times carried the news of Roentgen's work on January 16, 1896 (and misspelled his name). Some scientists could have claimed prior discovery, had they been more observant. A Philadelphian, A. W. Goodspeed, showed an X-ray photograph he had accidentally made six years earlier, but he sought no credit, admitting he had not realized what he had done.

HIDDEN SOLIDS REVEALED

Prof. Routgen's Experiments with Crookes's Vacuum Tube.

BULLETS FOUND BY USING LIGHT

Opaque Bodies Covered by Other Bodies Photographed — Views of Profs. O. N. Rood and Halleck of Columbia.

Men of science in this city are awaiting with the utmost impatience the arrival of European technical journals, which will give them the full particulars of Prof. Routgen's great discovery of a method of photographing opaque bodies covered by other bodies, hitherto regarded as wholly impenetrable by light rays of any kind.

Prof. Routgen of Würzburg University has recently discovered a light which, for

A RELUCTANT HERO OF SCIENCE
Wilhelm Conrad Roentgen was a professor at the University of Würzburg when he stumbled upon X-rays by noticing how they made fluorescent material glow. When he published his findings, he became a national hero overnight. He was decorated by Kaiser Wilhelm II but, preferring science to glory, he turned down a title of nobility offered to him by the Prince of Bavaria.

"LOOKING" AT A BROKEN BONE

At Dartmouth College one of the first medical uses of X-rays was made on February 3, 1896, by Dr. Gilman Frost *(right)* and his brother Dr. Edwin Frost, shown above X-raying a patient's broken arm—unaware of the dangers of prolonged exposure. The crude equipment consists of a battery, a cathode-ray tube (illuminated), an induction coil and film (under the boy's arm).

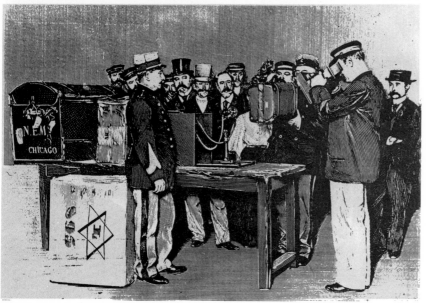

"LOOKING" THROUGH LUGGAGE

This photograph, taken in August 1897, shows French customs officials using a fluoroscope to "see" inside travelers' luggage. A fluoroscope has a screen coated with material that glows when struck by X-rays, thus providing, in effect, a "live" picture. The fluoroscopic use of X-rays was refined soon after Roentgen's discovery and is still an extensive practice in medicine.

Pierre Curie as a teacher at the Sorbonne.

Radioactivity and the Family That Tracked It Down

In 1896 in Paris, Henri Becquerel noticed that uranium, with no external stimulation, emitted radiation which would fog a film just as X-rays did. Thus was radioactivity discovered, and it launched the extraordinary careers of Pierre and Marie Curie, who shared with Becquerel a Nobel Prize for the discovery. The Curies went on with more intensive research and in 1898 discovered radium and polonium, by far the most radioactive elements then known. For this Marie won another Nobel Prize and became the only person ever to be so honored twice.

The Curies' daughter and son-in-law, Irène and Frédéric Joliot-Curie, followed the same path and won further honors for their own work in radioactivity (*far right*). But the cost of these contributions was high: Marie, Irène and Frédéric all died as victims of the effects of radioactivity.

A FACE OF "TERRIBLE PATIENCE"
Intense but serene, Marie Curie's face reflects what her daughter Eve called the "terrible patience" she displayed during her tedious radium experiments. Eve, the one nonscientist in the family, wrote the celebrated biography of her mother, and in it described her manifold talents as "a physicist, a chemist, a specialized worker, an engineer and a laboring man all at once."

184

ACCLAIM FROM AMERICA
Marie and Irène Curie flank President Warren G. Harding during a 1921 ceremony when he presented them with a gram of radium for their experiments. Money to buy the radium—then worth $100,000 a gram—had been raised in a campaign by Mrs. William Brown Meloney *(far left)*, a New York newspaper editor. Funds left over provided Mme. Curie with a life income.

SECOND-GENERATION HONORS
Irène and Frédéric Joliot-Curie receive the 1935 Nobel Prize for chemistry from the King of Sweden, Gustav V, for their work in producing radioactive elements artificially. Irène was later awarded the French Legion of Honor, in 1939. Because Pierre and Marie Curie had no male heir, their son-in-law added the name Curie to his own so that its fame would not die out.

A Generation
of Genius Launches
a New Age

Discovery of X-rays and radioactivity presented physicists with a perplexing problem. The accepted concept of the atom as a tiny, solid billiard ball did not provide for any mysterious emissions, and yet the newly found radiation was just that—a throwing-off of energy and matter.

In a period of unparalleled international interest, scientists everywhere set to work on this puzzle. In America Thomas Edison and others explored new X-ray techniques *(right center)*. In England an exuberant New Zealander named Ernest Rutherford *(right)* led British physicists into a period of glittering success. In 1911 he discovered the nucleus and came up with a new structural concept of the atom which is still valid today. This paved the way for the great advances in atomic physics made by such men as the Dane, Niels Bohr. Also in 1911, radiation was the theme of an international conference at Brussels. A later conference in 1933 on the subject of the nucleus brought together most of the scientists then leading the way into the atomic age. In 1938 two German chemists *(far right)* opened the door on that age when they split the atom of the radioactive element uranium.

"THE NURSERY OF GENIUS"
Such was the nickname given the Cavendish Laboratory at Cambridge, England, where Ernest—later Lord—Rutherford *(right)* presided for 18 brilliant years. Cavendish, congenial and stimulating, was an inspiration to science in the early 20th Century, when no fewer than 10 Nobel Prize winners worked within its walls.

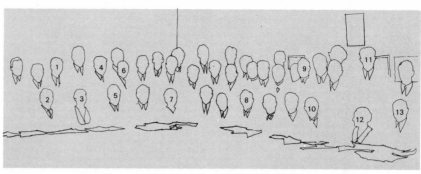

FRÉDÉRIC JOLIOT-CURIE (1)
ERWIN SCHRÖDINGER (2)
IRÉNE JOLIOT-CURIE (3)
WERNER HEISENBERG (4)
NIELS BOHR (5)
ENRICO FERMI (6)
MARIE SKLODOWSKA CURIE (7)
LORD RUTHERFORD (8)
SIR JOHN DOUGLAS COCKCROFT (9)
PRINCE LOUIS VICTOR DE BROGLIE (10)
ERNEST ORLANDO LAWRENCE (11)
LISE MEITNER (12)
SIR JAMES CHADWICK (13)

A STAR-STUDDED ASSEMBLAGE

The Solvay Institute in Brussels has played host to prestigious international science meetings since it was endowed by a Belgian philanthropist in 1912. The 1933 conference *(left)* had a particularly eminent roster, led by French physicist Paul Langevin, including 20 Nobel Prize winners. Thirteen distinguished scientists whose achievements are noted elsewhere in this book are identified in the key above.

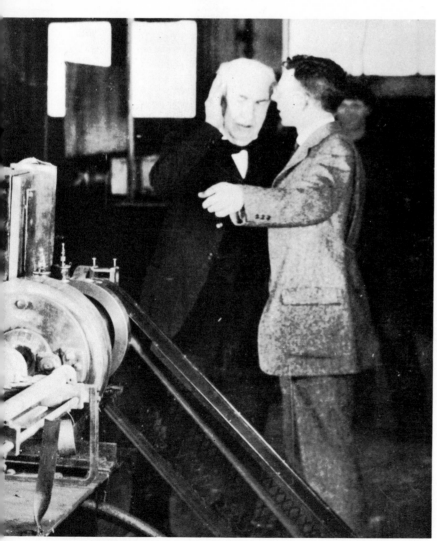

THE VANGUARD OF ATOMIC ENERGY

Otto Hahn *(right)* and Fritz Strassmann stand at the worktable where they split the uranium nucleus in 1938. Fortunately for the Allies in World War II, the Germans failed to capitalize on their breakthrough; physicists in America were the first to translate the significance of a nuclear fission into the reality of an atom bomb.

PIONEERS IN X-RAY TECHNIQUES

W. D. Coolidge shows Thomas Edison a machine in Schenectady, New York, for making tungsten filaments for X-ray tubes. By discovering how to make tungsten flexible, Coolidge in 1913 made possible the modern X-ray tube. Edison himself had already done extensive work on fluorescent materials for use with X-rays.

187

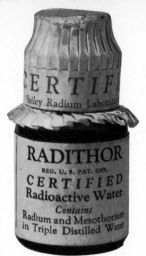

A Dark and Dangerous Force

The deadly nature of X-rays and radioactivity was so little understood at first that man paid a painful price to discover how potent a force he had unleashed. Not until the mid-1920s was there wide realization that X-rays and radioactivity's alpha, beta and gamma rays can destroy the tissues of flesh and bone and cause genetic aberrations by ravaging the reproductive cells. In blithe ignorance of all this, men unwittingly exposed themselves to maiming and death. Even the great Thomas Edison was unaware of the danger: his assistant, Clarence Dally, died in 1905 from overexposure suffered in innumerable X-ray experiments. Radium was hailed by many as a great healer. It went into patent medicines with awful results *(left)* and generally was treated with tragic—and often fatal—carelessness *(below)*. Even as late as 1954 man's hard-won lessons in the dangers of radiation were not enough to prevent mishaps in dealing with it *(opposite)*.

Far from being solved today, the radiation peril looms larger as atomic energy is used more and more in both peaceful and military roles. All nuclear fission, destructive or useful, creates radioactive by-products. Protecting ourselves from their invisible lethal radiation is one of the most profound problems of our age.

A DEADLY PANACEA

Radithor—a liquid patent medicine containing radioactive salts—was sold as a "harmless" cure for over 160 ailments. But when, in 1932, a Pittsburgh businessman died a slow, horrible death after having drunk several bottles a day for four years, the furor forced Radithor's producer to flee the country. Financial ruin followed for many makers of radium products.

GIMCRACKS AND QUACKERY

Medical quacks rushed to get on the radioactive bandwagon. Contraptions such as this thorium inhaler were touted as cure-alls for everything from arthritis to nearsightedness. One fanatical doctor said radium fulfilled a Biblical prophecy and urged its liberal use as a medical and moral force. He called it "the gentlest and most soothing healer the world has known."

A TRAGEDY OF INNOCENCE

Unaware of their peril, these technicians engaged in purifying radium are leaning, without protection, over open dishes of radium salts. They are unknowingly getting dangerous doses of radiation which, after a continued exposure over many years, will cause irreparable damage. Similar exposure by radium watch-dial painters during World War I caused at least 40 deaths.

AN H-BOMB'S FEARFUL LEGACY
The 1954 nuclear test blast at Bikini in the Pacific caused much more radioactive fallout than was expected. A wind shift carried the "dirty" residue over a Japanese fishing vessel and badly contaminated its crew *(above)*. One death resulted; had the ship been 10 miles closer to the blast, the rest of the 23 men aboard would have succumbed to radiation injuries.

RADIATION VICTIM
Sanjiro Masouda, being tested *(right)* for radioactivity with a Geiger counter, spent 16 grim months in a hospital after the Bikini miscalculation. He described himself as a "great worm in the process of putrefaction." Each sailor got $4,500 from the U.S. After the blast, Japanese fisheries had to condemn 213,000 pounds of radioactive fish taken from Pacific waters.

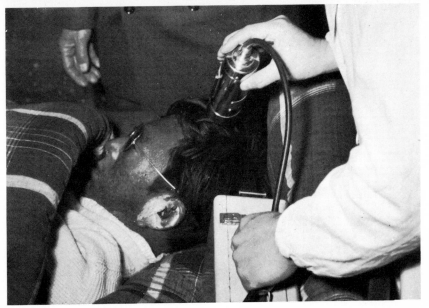

TRACKING A MOSQUITO

These mosquitoes are being examined for radio-activity with a Geiger counter. They were bred in California's Central Valley in ponds treated with radiophosphorus. In subsequent wanderings they carried the isotope with them until caught. Here the distinctive radiation from the isotope is being identified, thus providing a record of the insects' range and travel patterns.

A Bright and Beneficent Force

For all its sinister aspects, radiation is not entirely the work of the devil. It can also be a force for good. X-rays, for instance, are one of medicine's most valuable adjuncts when properly handled, and radiotherapy has long been used to treat certain kinds of cancer and blindness. A newer and potentially even more beneficial use for radioactivity is as a telltale tracer for analyzing complex chemical processes such as plant and animal growth. Certain basically stable elements can be atomically rearranged to make them artificially radioactive. These mutations are called radioisotopes, and each one has a distinctive radiation which can be easily traced and identified by such instruments as Geiger counters. When a minute quantity of an isotope—as little as one trillionth of a gram—is added to the food of an animal or fertilizer of a plant, it will send out a continuous report on the movement of its carrier through the growth process. This radioactive "eye" is also being focused on all manner of problems, ranging from pest control to heart disease *(left)*.

Radioisotopes are produced by nuclear fission in an atomic pile, and the same energy-producing reaction can be used to light cities or drive ships' turbines *(opposite)*. Radiation has already been brought under enough control to make these operations perfectly safe, and it will undoubtedly be tamed even more. But we will never again be without it. It is, in a sense, the heartbeat of the atomic age.

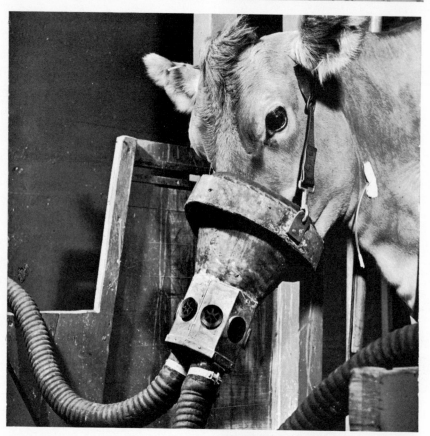

TRACING SECRETS OF GROWTH

This cow does not seem to care, but it is "hot." It has been injected with a nutrient containing the isotope radiocarbon, and is now exhaling radioactive carbon dioxide which can be analyzed. The rate at which the radioactive tracer is exhaled shows how fast the cow's body is using the injected substances and offers evidence of which foods are best for healthy growth.

HELP FOR THE HEART

The Bermuda toad excretes from a neck gland a substance called bufagin which is almost identical to the heart drug digitalis. By feeding the toads "hot" algae, doctors can make the bufagin radioactive. They can then use this as a tracer, with its telltale radiation, to help determine the exact effects of digitalis-type drugs on the actions and tissues of the human heart.

STRONG, SILENT POWER

The nuclear submarine U.S.S. *Patrick Henry* represents the modern dream of transportation power. Its atomic reactor, shielded to prevent radiation danger, generates heat to make steam for the turbines. No oxygen is needed for the reactor, so the boat can stay submerged for weeks. Extensive use of atomic power is also in view for undersea tankers and surface ships.

The Needless Muddle of Our Weights and Measures

MAN GAUGES length and breadth, weight and volume, heat and cold by arbitrary standards of comparison. Early Egyptians measured liquid volume by the mouthful; medieval Englishmen measured length by the yard—defined as the distance from the tip of their king's nose to the end of his hand. In the 18th Century France adopted the metric system of weights and measures. This established three basic units: the meter (for distance), liter (for volume) and gram (for mass or weight). The French system took hold on the Continent, as did the Centigrade temperature scale devised by the Swedish astronomer Andres Celsius, which set the freezing point of water at 0° and its boiling point at 100°.

England went its own way, with its American colonies tagging along. It continued to rely on the Fahrenheit temperature scale (on which water freezes at 32°, boils at 212°) and on such traditional measurements as the inch, foot, yard and a host of oddities. Americans still employ 85 different weights and measures, including the chain, furlong, league, gill, peck, bushel, dram, cord, two kinds of pound, ton, ounce, quart and mile.

Attempts to change the U.S. over to the metric system began in George Washington's time and persist today. The National Bureau of Standards uses samples of the international standard meter and kilogram (bars made of platinum and iridium) to check our own measurements. Our scientists use the metric system to conform to worldwide professional custom; some drug products are being labeled by metric measure. This trend, and the obvious benefits to foreign trade if there were global unanimity on weights and measures, may yet compel the U.S. to "go metric." Until then conversion tables such as the one below will be needed to reconcile confusions.

Metric to Metric

Length
- 1 millimeter = .001 meter
- 1 centimeter = .01 meter
- 1 decimeter = .1 meter
- 1 meter = 1,000 millimeters
  - 100 centimeters
  - 10 decimeters
- 1 decameter = 10 meters
- 1 hectometer = 100 meters
- 1 kilometer = 1,000 meters

Area (land)
- 1 are = 100 square meters
- 1 hectare = 100 ares

Volume
- 1 cubic centimeter = 1,000 cubic millimeters
- 1 cubic decimeter = 1,000 cubic centimeters
- 1 cubic meter = 1,000 cubic decimeters

Dry and liquid measure of capacity
- (1 liter = 1 cubic decimeter)
- 1 liter = 1,000 milliliters
  - 100 centiliters
  - 10 deciliters
- 1 kiloliter = 1,000 liters

Mass (weight)
- 1 gram = 1,000 milligrams
  - 100 centigrams
  - 10 decigrams
- 1 kilogram = 1,000 grams
- 1 metric ton = 1,000 grams

Metric to English

Length
- 1 millimeter = .03937 inch
- 1 centimeter = .3937 inch
- 1 decimeter = 3.937 inches
- 1 meter = 39.37 inches
  - 3.281 feet
  - 1.094 yards
- 1 decameter = 10.94 yards
- 1 hectometer = 109.4 yards
- 1 kilometer = .6214 mile

Area (land)
- 1 are = 119.6 square yards
- 1 hectare = 2.471 acres

Volume
- 1 cubic meter = 35.31 cubic feet
  - 1.038 cubic yards

Dry and liquid measure of capacity
- 1 liter = 1.057 liquid quarts
  - 0.908 dry quart
- 1 kiloliter = 264.2 gallons
  - 113.5 pecks
  - 28.38 bushels

Mass (weight)
- 1 gram = .03527 avdp. ounce
  - .0322 troy ounce
- 1 kilogram = 2.205 avdp. pounds
  - 2.679 troy pounds
- 1 metric ton = 1.1023 short tons
  - .9842 long ton

English to Metric

Length
- 1 inch = 25.40 millimeters
- 1 foot = 30.48 centimeters
- 1 yard = .9144 meter
- 1 mile = 1.609 kilometers

Area (land)
- 1 square yard = 0.8361 square meter
- 1 acre = .4047 hectare

Volume
- 1 cubic foot = 28.32 cubic decimeter
- 1 cubic yard = .7646 cubic meter

Dry and liquid measure of capacity
- 1 liquid pint = .4732 liter
- 1 dry pint = .5506 liter
- 1 liquid quart = 0.9463 liter
- 1 dry quart = 1.1012 liters
- 1 gallon = 3.785 liters
- 1 peck = 8.8096 liters
- 1 bushel = 35.24 liters

Mass (weight)
- 1 avdp. ounce = 28.35 grams
- 1 troy ounce = 31.10 grams
- 1 avdp. pound = .4536 kilogram
- 1 troy pound = .3732 kilogram
- 1 short ton = .9072 metric ton
- 1 long ton = 1.016 metric tons

A COMPARISON OF SYSTEMS

Metric and English equivalents for familiar weights and measures are presented in the conversion table above. In the left-hand column are units of the metric system, based on simple multiples of 10, making metric computations quick and easy. In the center column, English equivalents of standard metric units are given; at the right are the metric equivalents of standard English measures. The English system has two sets of units of weight: precious stones, precious metals and drugs are weighed in "troy" units; all other commodities are weighed in "avoirdupois" units.

POSITIVE PARTICLE ACCELERATORS

YEAR	NAME	COST	PARTICLE	PATH	SIZE	OPERATING ENERGY (MILLIONS OF ELECTRON VOLTS)
1936	**37-INCH CYCLOTRON** University of California, Berkeley, Calif.	**$50,000**	**DEUTERON ALPHA**		37-inch diameter	**DEUTERON** 8 **ALPHA** 16
1939	**60-INCH CYCLOTRON** University of California, Berkeley, Calif.	**$225,000**	**PROTON DEUTERON ALPHA**		60-inch diameter	**PROTON** 12 **DEUTERON** 24 **ALPHA** 48
1946	**SYNCHRO-CYCLOTRON** University of California, Berkeley, Calif.	**$1,400,000**	**PROTON DEUTERON ALPHA He³**		184-inch diameter	**PROTON** 735 **DEUTERON** 460 **ALPHA** 915 **He³** 1,140
1952	**COSMOTRON** (proton-synchroton) Brookhaven National Laboratory, Upton, N.Y.	**$7,000,000**	**PROTON**		75-foot diameter	**3,000**
1954	**BEVATRON** (protron-synchrotron) University of California, Berkeley, Calif.	**$9,500,000**	**PROTON**		110-foot diameter	**6,300**
1957	**SYNCHROPHASOTRON** (proton-synchrotron) Dubna, USSR	estimates vary from **$34,000,000** to **$100,000,000**	**PROTON**		200-foot diameter	**10,000**
1959	**C.E.R.N. PROTON-SYNCHROTRON** Geneva, Switzerland	**$35,000,000**	**PROTON**		656-foot diameter	**28,000**
1960	**ALTERNATING GRADIENT PROTON-SYNCHROTRON** Brookhaven National Laboratory, Upton, N.Y.	**$33,000,000**	**PROTON**		850-foot diameter	**33,000**

ELECTRON ACCELERATORS

YEAR	NAME	COST	PARTICLE	PATH	SIZE	OPERATING ENERGY
1950	**BETATRON** University of Illinois, Urbana, Ill.	**$1,500,000**	**ELECTRON**		8-foot diameter	**300**
1954	**MARK III LINEAR ACCELERATOR** Stanford University, Stanford, Calif.	**$6,900,000**	**ELECTRON**		300 feet long	1954: **700** 1960: **1,000**
1954	**CORNELL SYNCHROTRON** Cornell University, Ithaca, N.Y.	**$500,000** **$1,000,000**	**ELECTRON**		50-foot diameter	1954: **1,400** 1963: **2,200**
1962	**CAMBRIDGE SYNCHROTRON** Harvard-M.I.T., Cambridge, Mass.	**$12,000,000**	**ELECTRON**		236-foot diameter	**6,400**
estimated 1967	**TWO-MILE LINEAR ACCELERATOR** Stanford University, Stanford, Calif.	estimated **$114,000,000**	**ELECTRON**		10,000 feet long	**20,000**

TYPE	FIELD	OTHER DETAILS
85-TON WEAK FOCUSING MAGNET	FIELD STEADY WITH TIME	E. O. Lawrence built the first experimental cyclotron in 1932 and followed it with 9-, 11- and 27½-inch machines before building the three larger ones shown here.
225-TON WEAK FOCUSING MAGNET	FIELD STEADY WITH TIME	This machine's high-intensity beam (great number of particles) was instrumental in the discovery of seven new elements. It is no longer in operation *(page 158)*.
4,000-TON WEAK FOCUSING MAGNET	FIELD STEADY WITH TIME	This cyclotron, modified to cope with the unusual behavior of particles at higher Mev energies, produced the first pions, particles which hold the nucleus together.
2,000-TON WEAK FOCUSING MAGNET	FIELD INCREASES WITH TIME	The cosmotron figures prominently in studying mesons and the so-called strange particles—mysterious bits of matter created by forceful bombardment of the nucleus.
9,700-TON WEAK FOCUSING MAGNET	FIELD INCREASES WITH TIME	Named for its Bev range, the bevatron dramatically succeeded in fulfilling its specific function: the discovery of the theoretically predicted particle called an antiproton.
36,000-TON WEAK FOCUSING MAGNET	FIELD INCREASES WITH TIME	A scaled-up bevatron, this machine is designed on the weak-focusing principle which, for energies in this high range, requires impractically heavy and costly magnets.
3,530-TON STRONG FOCUSING MAGNET	FIELD INCREASES WITH TIME	Built by the International *Centre Européen pour la Recherche Nucléaire,* this machine, with one tenth the synchrophasotron's magnet weight, has 2.8 times its energy.
4,000-TON STRONG FOCUSING MAGNET	FIELD INCREASES WITH TIME	The biggest accelerator in the world, Brookhaven's AGS *(pages 160-165)* costs yearly over $10 million to operate, has not yet reached its vast experimental potential.
400-TON MAGNET	FIELD INCREASES WITH TIME	This machine, named after beta rays which are streams of electrons, produces high-energy X-rays. Smaller machines of the same type produce X-rays for medical use.
NO MAGNETS NEEDED	NO MAGNETS NEEDED	The Mark III was 220 feet long at first, but was lengthened in 1959. Its electron beam determines the magnetic and electrical properties of neutrons and protons.
1954: 20-TON MAGNET / 1963: 50-TON MAGNET	FIELD INCREASES WITH TIME	This accelerator preceded the positive-particle machines in employing the strong-focusing principle. It has now been rebuilt several times to step up its energy output.
350-TON STRONG FOCUSING MAGNET	FIELD INCREASES WITH TIME	This device nears the practical energy limit for accelerating electrons in a circular orbit. More acceleration results in a prohibitive loss of energy through radiation.
NO MAGNETS NEEDED	NO MAGNETS NEEDED	This giant machine will provide unparalleled precision for measuring the smallest subatomic particles, and scientists predict that it will create still-unknown forms of matter.

MAGNETS: across top of table.

Atom-Smashers: A Roster of Champions

The particle accelerator *(pages 158-167)* is to nuclear physics what the telescope is to astronomy. Streams of high-energy particles provide the only way of "looking" into the atom's nucleus, and scientists' demand for ever more powerful "eyes" has spurred the evolution of particle-accelerating techniques. The genealogy on these pages compares some of the elite among atom-smashers. They are in two groups: those accelerating positive particles and those accelerating negatively charged electrons.

The Cockcroft-Walton machine *(page 162)* and one designed by R. J. Van de Graaff at Princeton University in the early 1930s were the first significant steps toward today's high-energy giants. Then came the cyclotron *(left)*, the first machine to use the same accelerating station over and over to impart energy cumulatively to orbiting particles. These spiral out from the center with increasing velocity, moving in a plane between two solid magnets which provide a steady controlling field. A longer spiral path will result in higher energies, but soon the magnets —which must embrace the whole path area from center to circumference—get prohibitively large and costly.

The cosmotron solved this problem by the use of a circular rather than spiral path. Smaller, separate magnets placed around the circumference need affect only the narrow track of the orbit. The field strength does not remain steady but increases to cope with the orbiting particles' rising velocity. Also providing for more energy with less magnet weight is the strong-focusing principle. By controlling the particles' orbit more efficiently *(pages 163-165)*, strong focusing has made possible the prodigious energy outputs of the Geneva and Brookhaven synchrotrons.

The last five machines listed are designed to supply high-energy electrons for nuclear research. The betatron uses the same magnet both to constrain the particles and to accelerate them (all the others use an electric accelerating force). Synchrotrons effectively accelerate electrons to moderately high energies, but for very high energies the only possible apparatus is the linear accelerator, which needs no magnets at all *(pages 166-167)*.

BIBLIOGRAPHY

General

*Beiser, Arthur, *The World of Physics*. McGraw-Hill, 1960.

Gamow, George, *Matter, Earth and Sky*. Prentice-Hall, 1958.

*Lessing, Lawrence P., *Understanding Chemistry*. John Wiley & Sons, 1959.

Pollack, Philip, *Careers and Opportunities in Chemistry*. E. P. Dutton, 1960.

Pollack, Philip, *Careers and Opportunities in Physics*. E. P. Dutton, 1961.

†Russell, Bertrand, *The Analysis of Matter*. Dover, 1954.

Toulmin, Stephen and June Goodfield, *The Architecture of Matter*. Harper & Row, 1963.

Historical

Aitchison, Leslie, *A History of Metals* (2 vols.). John Wiley & Sons, 1960.

†Bleich, Alan Ralph, *The Story of X-rays from Röntgen to Isotopes*. Dover, 1960.

†Broglie, Louis de, *The Revolution in Physics*. Farrar, Straus & Cudahy, 1953.

*Butterfield, Herbert, *Origins of Modern Science*, Macmillan, 1957.

†Dampier, Sir William Cecil, *A Shorter History of Science*. Meridian, 1957.

†Jaffe, Bernard, *Crucibles: The Story of Chemistry*. Fawcett, 1960.

†Jeans, Sir James, *The Growth of Physical Science*. Fawcett, 1948.

Larsen, Egon, *The Cavendish Laboratory*. Franklin Watts, 1962.

*Melsen, Andrew G. van, *From Atomos to Atom*. Duquesne University Press, 1952.

*Partington, James R., *A Short History of Chemistry*. St. Martin's Press, 1957.

†Read, John. *Through Alchemy to Chemistry*. Harper & Row, 1963.

*Stillman, John Maxson, *The Story of Alchemy and Early Chemistry*. Peter Smith, 1962.

†Taylor, F. Sherwood, *The Alchemists*. Collier, 1962.

†Taylor, Lloyd W. and Forrest G. Tucker, *Physics, the Pioneer Science* (2 vols.). Dover, 1959.

Biography

*Curie, Eve, *Madame Curie*. Doubleday, 1949.

Curie, Marie, *Pierre Curie* (Translated by Charlotte and Vernon Kellogg). Macmillan, 1923.

Farber, Eduard, *Nobel Prize Winners in Chemistry, 1901-1961*. Abelard-Schuman, 1962.

Gamow, George, *Biography of Physics*. Harper & Row, 1961.

Garrett, Alfred B., *The Flash of Genius*. D. Van Nostrand, 1963.

Glasser, Otto, *Dr. W. C. Röntgen*. Charles C. Thomas, 1958.

Heathcote, Niels H. de V., *Nobel Prize Winners in Physics, 1901-1950*. Abelard-Schuman, 1954.

Holmyard, Eric J., *Makers of Chemistry*. Oxford University Press, 1931.

Special Fields

*Asimov, Isaac, *The World of Carbon*. Abelard-Schuman, 1958.

*Asimov, Isaac, *The World of Nitrogen*. Abelard-Schuman, 1958.

†Davis, Kenneth S. and John Arthur Day, *Water, the Mirror of Science*. Doubleday, 1961.

†Dietz, David H., *Atomic Science, Bombs, and Power*. Collier, 1962.

Frisch, Otto R., *Atomic Physics Today*. Basic Books, 1961.

†Gamow, George, *The Atom and Its Nucleus*. Prentice-Hall, 1961.

Hawley, Gessner G., *Small Wonder: the Story of Colloids*. Alfred A. Knopf, 1947.

Hecht, Selig, *Explaining the Atom*. Viking Press, 1954.

†Holden, Alan and Phylis Singer, *Crystals and Crystal Growing*. Doubleday, 1960.

*King, Thomson, *Water, Miracle of Nature*. Macmillan, 1953.

†MacDonald, D.K.C., *Near Zero*. Doubleday, 1961.

Merton, Thomas, *Original Child Bomb*. New Directions, 1962.

*Meyer, Jerome S., *The Elements*. World, 1957.

†Romer, Alfred, *The Restless Atom*. Doubleday, 1960.

*Schubert, Jack and Ralph E. Lapp, *Radiation*. Viking Press, 1957.

Seaborg, Glenn T., *The Transuranium Elements*. Addison-Wesley, 1958.

Seaborg, Glenn T. and Evans G. Valens, *Elements of the Universe*. E. P. Dutton, 1958.

†Valentine, J. M., *A Layman's Guide to Atomic Physics*. Collier, 1962.

*Also available in paperback edition

†Only available in paperback edition

ACKNOWLEDGMENTS

The editors of this book are indebted to Dr. Harry B. Gray, Associate Professor of Chemistry at Columbia University, Dr. Charles K. Bockelman, Associate Professor of Physics at Yale University and Dr. Winston H. Bostick, Professor of Physics at Stevens Institute of Technology, who served as general consultants, and to the following persons and institutions: Arthur Beiser; Donald Blake, Linde Company, Union Carbide Corporation; Harold Brayman and Dr. Carleton Sperati, E.I. du Pont de Nemours and Company; Eileen Carson, Lawrence Radiation Laboratory, University of California, Berkeley; Eugene Cone, American Institute of Physics; Dr. Dale R. Corson, Cornell University; D. D. Cowen, P. B. Orr, M. E. Ramsey, Dr. Arthur F. Rupp and Wallace N. Tillery, Oak Ridge National Laboratory; Dr. Adrian H. Daane, Iowa State University; Dr. Allen G. Debus, University of Chicago; Douglas Dupen, Stanford Linear Accelerator, Stanford University; Dr. J. F. Eichelberger, Mound Laboratory, Monsanto Research Corporation; Dr. Merril Eisenbud, New York University Medical Center; Dr. Paul R. Fields, Argonne National Laboratory; Dr. Warren Goodel, Columbia University; Robert Hedges, Allied Chemical Corporation; Lazare Kaplan & Sons, Inc.; Dr. Milton Kerker, Clarkson College of Technology; J. N. Kinn, IBM; Howard E. Kremers, American Potash and Chemical Corporation; Dr. Alfred Leitner, Michigan State University; L. Dale McCowen, Michigan Chemical Corporation; John Mason and Frank Scott, Union Carbide Plastics Company; Richard Meacham, Radium Chemical Company, Inc.; Joseph Monigle, Hagley Museum; John H. Munier, Corning Glass Works; Marguerite Perey, Strasbourg Nuclear Research Center; William W. Pomeroy, NASA; Lawrence Pugh, Ervan Lucas Bols Distilling Company; Dennis Puleston and Dr. Martin Plotkin, Brookhaven National Laboratory; Harriet Raymond, Celanese Plastics Company; F. T. Richardson, U.S. Atomic Energy Commission; Dr. Clark Robinson, University of Illinois; Dr. Edward N. Rosenquist, Dayton Laboratory, Monsanto Research Corporation; Dr. Vincent Schaefer; Professor Jack H. Schulman, Columbia University; Dr. Ivan Simon, Arthur D. Little, Inc.; Dr. Frank H. Spedding, Ames Laboratory, Iowa State University; Dr. Jack Steinberger, Columbia University; Dr. Z. John Stekly and Vincent Coates, Avco-Everett Research Laboratory; Dr. Walther Stoeckenius, The Rockefeller Institute; Bruce E. Strasser, Bell Telephone Laboratories, Inc.; Dr. Curry Street, Harvard University; Langdon P. Williams, The Society of the Plastics Industry, Inc.; Dr. William J. Young, Museum of Fine Arts, Boston.

INDEX

Numerals in italics indicate a photograph or painting of the subject mentioned.

PICTURE CREDITS

Credits for pictures from left to right are separated by commas, top to bottom by dashes.

PRODUCTION STAFF FOR TIME INCORPORATED

Arthur R. Murphy Jr. (Vice President and Director of Production), Robert E. Foy, James P. Menton and Caroline Ferri
Text photocomposed under the direction of Albert J. Dunn and Arthur J. Dunn

X

Printed by R. R. Donnelley & Sons Company, Crawfordsville, Indiana
Lithography by Livermore and Knight Co., a division of Printing Corporation of America, Providence, Rhode Island
Bound by R. R. Donnelley & Sons Company, Crawfordsville, Indiana
Paper by The Mead Corporation, Dayton, Ohio